first time Mom

by Wendy Beahn

CMB Production

Cover and book design by Dorothy Hogan
Author photo courtesy of Kate and Steve Ball

Library of Congress Control Number: 2001127009
Beahn, Wendy.
first time Mom.
1. Pregnancy   2. Motherhood   3. Childbirth
4. Mother & Infant   5. Health & Hygiene

ISBN 0-9715209-0-9 (paperback)

TO ORDER

Copies of *first time Mom* can be purchased through the Web site
firsttimeMomOnline.com. Additional copies can be purchased through
U.S. mail by sending a money order or check for $15.90 ($10.95 + $4.95
tax and shipping – see order form on last page) to:

CMB Production
P.O. Box 815
Hilliard, OH 43026

Note: The information contained in this book is not intended to substitute for
advice that you might receive from your doctor or your child's physician. Always
seek the advice of your doctor.

This book is dedicated to the first time mom who will experience one of the most magical events of her life. May you revel in the joys of being a mom and cherish every moment of your child's life.

This book is also dedicated:

To my wonderful baby, Colin Michael, who is the reason I write this book.

To my teammate, husband, and love of my life, Dave.

To my inspiration: my Mom.

To my sisters: Linda and Deb.

To my dear friend Amy for her encouragement and support.

To my heroes, Judy and Gina, who truly prepared me for this whole experience.

Who am I? I'm a first time mom who could not have been any more clueless about having a baby. Looking back, I pretty much knew that the tape on the diaper goes from the back to the front. That's about it. Of course, I read books about healthy eating and pregnancy, but I never thought about birth and beyond. While talking to a mom about my worries over being pregnant, she replied:

> "Don't worry about the pregnancy part. Your body will take care of that. Worry about after the baby comes. Nothing prepares you for that!"

It hit me like a ton of bricks. So wrapped up with the pregnancy and designing the nursery I had not even thought of what would happen once the baby arrived. I began my quest for information as I talked to my friends and family who had children. What I learned from our talks helped prepare me for the birth and life with a baby.

This information was so useful I thought about passing it on to my girlfriends who had not had a baby yet. That's when I decided to write a book containing this information, along with what I experienced. *first time Mom* discusses what I learned about labor, delivery and life with a baby for the first six months. It also includes tips, hints, suggestions, recommendations, experiences, and the humor in being a first time mom. I also included a section in the back of the book called My Book of Lists. This part offers various detailed checklists to help a first time mom prepare for baby's arrival.

Good luck and enjoy being a first time mom!

Contents

GETTING IN YOUR GROOVE

MY BOOK OF LISTS

The Big Day

Chapter 1

Getting Ready to Go to the Hospital

I awoke with a jolt at 3:30 a.m. when I felt warm water trickle down my thigh. "Oh my God, I wet the bed!" I leaped out of bed with the pillow between my knees and waddled to the bathroom. Was I dreaming of going to the bathroom and just let go? How could I have peed? I was so embarrassed. As I was racing to the toilet, I noticed that no matter how hard I tried to hold it in, the liquid kept dripping down my legs onto the pillow. "Why won't it stop?," I thought. Then it dawned on me. I knew why. Just then, my husband, Dave, called out, "Are you OK?" In a voice mixed with nervousness and excitement, I replied, "I think my water just broke." I was one day over my due date.

I shuffled over to the toilet, pulled down my big maternity undies and sat down. I was so relieved to make it to the toilet, but low and behold, nothing was coming out. Dave came into the bathroom. I told him I wasn't sure if I had wet the bed or if my water broke. It felt like nothing was coming out, so I started to stand up. As I did, more warm water trickled out. I sat back down and nothing came out. When I tried to stand up again, more liquid dribbled out.

I couldn't do this much longer. I told Dave to get me a thick washcloth and another pair of underwear. He came back with both, so I took the washcloth and put it in the crotch of the underwear and put them on. At that point, I still wasn't sure if it was my water that broke or I had wet the bed. I guess I was afraid to acknowledge that my water had broken. I went back over to the bed and looked at the wet spot. It did not appear to be an odd color and when I smelled it, there was no odor. I went back into the bathroom and looked in the toilet. There were little white flakes float-ing around in the water. I remember in Lamaze class our teacher said to look for white flakes in the toilet. It was vernix caseosa, the pasty white stuff on babies that protects their skin while in the amniotic fluid.

"There were little white flakes in the toilet! My water had just broken. What the hell do I do next?" I thought. I told Dave I was pretty sure my water had broken. We looked at each other as if to say, "What should we do?" I never even felt a prick or pinch, nor was there any popping sound. I just started leaking.

We decided to call the emergency number for our doctor. Dave made the call and left the details and our telephone number with the answering service. About five minutes later, our doctor called. Dr. Morris was on call so we actual-ly got to talk to her. If it were another doctor, they would have been our point of contact until Dr. Morris got into the office. I wasn't feeling any contractions, but she said they could start anywhere from that point to an hour and a half. She said some people like to come in right away, while oth-ers want to remain within the comfort of their own home. Dr. Morris advised us to take morning rush hour traffic into consideration because any delays on the freeway could add another hour to our arrival at the hospital. She said if we decided to stay at home for a while, we should leave the house no later than 6:30 a.m. since we had to get on the free-way to get there. Nothing would be worse than sitting in traffic. I told her we would leave at 6:30 a.m. It was 4 a.m. I don't know why, but I asked her if we were going to have a baby today. She said, "Looks like it." My adrenaline started rushing.

We wanted to call everyone we knew but decided to hold off until 6 a.m. It was early, and I knew it was going to be a long day. I wanted to call my mom so bad, but I knew she would not be able to go back to sleep. I wanted her to get enough rest before the big event.

The next two and a half hours I spent getting ready. I took a shower, put on makeup, did my hair, got dressed, and put my overnight stuff in my packed bag. We got the camcorder, camera, pillows, and Lamaze bag all together in the living room. We added our overnight hospital bags to the pile. Since I had worked up until my due date, I changed my voice mail message and auto reply e-mail box. I left a voice mail message for my manager, Jason, and my office mate, Amy, letting them know we were leaving for the hospital.

Before we left, Dave ate a bowl of cereal, but I was not allowed to eat or drink anything. The Lamaze instructor warned not to put anything in your stomach once labor started because at some point it would most likely come back up. Little did I know that later in the day, I would prove that to be true. Dave let the dogs outside and then we fed them. It was Dave's responsibility to call the dog sitter from the hospital. She already had a key and was on standby.

Before I knew it, the clock read 6:15 a.m. The time had gone by so quickly. We were ready to leave, so Dave called his sister and I called my mom. The final call was to our assistant birth coach, my younger sister, Linda. She is our family's midwife, even though she was never medically trained. She was with my older sister, Deb, for the birth of all three of her boys, so Linda became our family "birthing baby pro."

I really wanted to have an additional person in the room because I knew there would be times when Dave would have to leave and I didn't want to be alone. Plus, I figured I'd need all the support and encouragement I could get. Dave initially wanted his best friend, Steve, to be there, but I reminded him that what was needed was support for me, not him.

While I talked to Linda, Dave hurriedly put our bags in the trunk of the car. It was 6:30 a.m. and he was getting jumpy. Dave whined: "We gotta go. Stop talking. We gotta go." He wanted to stick to the 6:30 a.m. timeframe and was getting very nervous and panicky. The car was packed, the dogs were taken care of, and we were all ready to go. As I waddled out to the car with my big belly sticking out like a beacon on a ship, I realized that the next time I came home, my life would be completely different. I would be a mom.

As we pulled out of the driveway, I felt a slight pressure about 2 inches below my belly button. It was a contraction! I wondered how long I had been having them. I was so wrapped up with getting ready and out the door I didn't even realize that my contractions had started. As we drove down the street, we went through the check list: camcorder, camera, car seat, Lamaze bag, my overnight bag, Dave's overnight bag, Lamaze pillows, purse, money – and we called Linda. We were ready. I had another contraction. It felt like I had gas and the pressure lasted about 30 seconds.

As we drove toward the freeway, I noticed my contractions had started getting stronger. At home, they were a slight pressure; when I got in the car they had progressed into feeling like gas and then graduated to a menstrual cramp-type pulling sensation. I found myself holding my breath until it was over. Dave noticed this and reminded me to start doing my breathing to get through them. This involved taking a half breath and then slowly exhaling. We practiced our breathing after Lamaze classes were over because I was afraid I would get lightheaded or pass out when I needed to use them. I didn't think my lungs were used to this kind of breathing.

I was so relieved we had practiced. When the next contraction came along, I started my breathing and Dave followed suit. What a sight we must have made. Surely we looked like two fish in a fish bowl, puffing away, wide-eyed, red-faced, and scared to death. My contraction was over. I looked at Dave. "It worked, the breathing worked." He looked relieved, but only for a moment.

We were so close to the freeway when we were snagged at a red light. As we sat there, I told Dave another contraction started, so he decided to time them. I started my breathing and focused on the clock on the dashboard, which read 6:42. I looked over at Dave and noticed he was wearing his Cleveland Indians baseball hat and was clean-shaven and handsome as ever. He looked like a dad. I don't know why I thought of that, but he looked like a dad. I also thought about how labor is glamorized in the movies, which portrays a half dressed husband dragging the bags to the car with the car keys pressed between his lips. While yelling and dashing around out of control, the woman stands there trying to figure out what the hell is wrong with him. Next, the man jumps in the car, puts it in reverse, screeches out of the driveway and speeds down the street. The wife is left standing in the driveway, arms folded, looking down the street waiting for it...the bright red brake lights, the white reverse lights and then the car screeching to a halt at the bottom of the driveway.

It hadn't happened like that for us, but the transformation occurred at that traffic light. As we sat there waiting, me puffing away, Dave's eyes glued to the clock, it happened. The contraction ended, Dave blinked, and then we got the green light. I could see it in his eyes. He looked at me and said, "Oh my God, your contractions are three minutes apart." He stomped on the gas, released the clutch, and I suddenly found myself in Mario Andretti's car. Our Honda Accord was transformed into a Porsche 911 and Dave's baseball hat magically changed into a helmet with a clear face shield. The car jumped forward with my whole body pressed into the seat as Dave shifted, 2, 3, 4, 5. We got on the freeway and you would have thought we were on the first turn of the Indy 500. It honestly felt like we were taking it on two wheels.

We flew down the freeway doing 75 mph. Determined to get us to the hospital on time, Mario weaved around traffic like a snake weaving around hot rocks in the desert sun. I knew we had plenty of time, so I calmly told him: "Dave, these contractions aren't even that strong. I'm not going to have the baby yet. Please slow down." But he was determined to complete his first responsibility with a stellar performance.

"We're going to have this baby on Route 270 if I don't get you to the hospital." Before I knew it, we entered curve two of the Indy 500 as Mario banked us around the ramp to get on 70 East. I had another contraction, focused on the clock, 6:52, and started breathing – aahh, heeeee, aahh, heeeee, aahh, heeeee. It was over after a minute.

I looked over at Dave just in time to see a look of disbelief wash over his face. Up ahead, the traffic slowed down around curve three. He down shifted, 4, 3, 2, and then the car was stopped on the freeway, and a slew of nasty words followed. I knew he was eyeing the berm and was mentally gauging what the ticket would cost and how many points it would be on his license. Now I knew I had to do something to distract him. I started talking about the names we had picked out. It worked. He redirected his attention and we started to chitchat about names, calling his family, and anything else I could think of. After we made it through the third curve, which always moves slowly due to the merging of two other freeways, we exited to High Street in downtown

Columbus. We were about 10 minutes away from the hospital but it was all downtown driving.

Mario felt slightly relieved since we were so close. He timed his way through traffic lights and weaved our way around people heading to work. It was interesting to know that day was just another normal day for so many people, but for us, it was a day we would never forget for the rest of our lives. There it was up ahead: Grant Medical Center, the hospital that would provide the most memorable, magical experience, far beyond our expectations.

What I learned about getting ready to go to the hospital:

- Make sure your Lamaze bag and overnight hospital bags are packed and ready to go three weeks before your due date. (See page 205 for a complete list of suggested items for both bags.)

- Arrange for pet care with family, friends, or a pet sitter. Make sure they have a key to your house with instructions regarding food and any special needs (i.e. medicine).

- If your water breaks, call your doctor. (If clear liquid is leaking and you can't hold it in, your water most likely has broken. Also look for white flakes in the toilet.)

- If you suspect you are having contractions (slight pressure, feelings of gas, or menstrual cramp-type pulling sensations in the stomach region) start timing them. When they are 5 minutes apart and last more than 30 seconds, call your doctor. (Confirm this with your doctor beforehand.)

- Consider waiting to call family and friends if it is the middle of the night. Most people will have a tough time going back to sleep, and it may be a long day.

- Notify anyone who will be in the delivery room with you before you leave for the hospital.

- If you are working up to your due date, leave your boss a voice mail, change your voice mail message, and activate e-mail auto reply letting everyone know you are now on maternity leave.

- Do not eat or drink anything.

- Start Lamaze breathing (half breath and slow exhale: aahh, heeee, aahh, heeee) to get through the contractions.

- Consider the time of day (rush hour, for example) when you decide to leave for the hospital.

- Make sure you both know the way to the hospital and where to park.

Chapter 2

Arriving at the Hospital

Dave slowed down the car in front of the hospital entrance and pulled into the valet parking line. "Screw it," he said. "We're using valet parking because I don't want you going very far and I want to be with you." Plus, he didn't want to have to come back down to the car after the baby was born and move it from emergency parking to general parking.

The valet parking was only $4 for the entire day and it was awesome. Unfortunately, there were two cars ahead of us, and Dave was getting impatient. "Where are they?" he exclaimed. True to a man's nature, he was impatient and pissed. Again I distracted him with questions about our bags in the back seat. That seemed to work. A few minutes later, it was our turn. We pulled up to the cheerful attendant and Dave gave him the ignition key. The man handed him a voucher, which he put in his wallet. Dave got my Lamaze bag and his "during labor" bag out of the back seat while I grabbed my Lamaze pillows. We headed into the hospital through the main entrance. It was so exciting because everyone looked at my belly, and looked at me, then Dave, and gave a big smile. I knew Dave wanted to grab the hospital intercom microphone and announce that we were here to have our baby. I was expecting The Ohio State University marching band to start playing. Since we went on a tour of the hospital two months earlier, we knew exactly where to go. We went straight to the elevator and up to the labor and delivery floor.

We approached the front desk and the check-in nurse asked if we were Wendy and Dave, which caught us off guard. She told us Dr. Morris called and told them we would be there around 7 a.m. Since I pre-registered about two months earlier, they had our paperwork on file and everything was ready to go. I'm so glad I had done that beforehand because at that moment I was extremely excited and my adrenaline was running so fast I would not have remembered my street address or phone number. After getting through a contraction and signing a few documents, a nurse took us to our labor room. It was 7:30 a.m. Along the way, I learned that I could no longer walk down the hallway while having a contraction. The pulling sensation was more intense with movement. I had to stop and hold on to the railing until the contraction was over.

What I learned about arriving at the hospital:

- Go on a tour of the hospital two months before your due date. **Write down:**
    - Where to park, what entrance to come in, and how to get to the labor and delivery floor. (You will never remember all this when the big day arrives.)
- Pre-register with the hospital two months before your due date so all paperwork is complete, on file, and ready when you walk in the door.
- Put your Lamaze bags and pillows in the back seat and lock your overnight bags in the trunk. Leave your overnight bags in the trunk until after the baby is born. It is one less thing to keep track of and haul from the labor room to your recovery room.

Chapter 3

Our Labor Room

Once we got to our room, our labor nurse, Jennifer, came in and introduced herself. She told me to take everything off and put on the hospital gown, which was lying on the bed. She provided a bag for me to put my street clothes in, said she would be back in a few minutes, and then left the room. Dave and I looked at each other. "Holy shit, we're having a baby!"

True to her word, Jennifer came back 10 minutes later, and I had an internal exam to see how far along I was. While lying in the bed slightly inclined, she told me to put the soles of my feet together. She performed an internal exam. Well, there went the modesty. I was 1 centimeter along. Jennifer put the monitor belt around my belly and the whole computer system came to life. The next thing I knew, the machine was spitting out paper with two squiggly lines on it. One recorded the baby's heartbeat and the other documented the level of my contractions. Another flashing light on the monitoring equipment was the baby's heart rate and a digital readout was the contraction level. Next Jennifer started my IV by pricking my left hand with a needle. I wasn't excited about that, but once I realized all the drugs were administered through it, I was all about making sure the IV was in place and ready.

About 15 minutes later, my sister, Linda (the veteran), came into the room looking like she had arrived at work. She was carrying a bag filled with snacks, a sweatshirt, a book, magazines, lip balm and gum. Linda acted like this was another day at the office, and she got busy. Her calmness, attention to detail, and anticipation of any needs proved to be a lifesaver to both Dave and me, who were clueless. She started out by putting my focal point, a Beanie Baby dog, on the portable table in front of the bed. Next, she showed Dave how to read the monitor to determine when a contraction was coming. When the digital number began to increase, it meant a contraction was starting. As the number decreased, it obviously meant the contraction was ending. That was extremely helpful because Dave was watching the monitor and could prepare me for the next contraction. I was able to focus on the Beanie Baby dog and get ready to start my breathing instead of being jolted into the breathing by a contraction.

Just then our nurse came in. Linda introduced herself and asked where the nurses' desk was and where the ice chips were. Linda also told Dave to get a good look at our nurse and remember her name, just in case we needed to find her. Jennifer said she would come back each hour to give me an internal exam. She told us she had three other moms to attend to, but she would be watching the monitor to track my progress. Jennifer pointed to a monitor with 16 squares and similar squiggly lines. She said there were monitors in each room, which allows the nurses to keep an eye on their patients. I knew the nurse was not in the room the whole time, thanks to my dear friend Judy. Judy had her baby a year ago and passed on the knowledge and experiences she went through. Therefore, I was not surprised when Jennifer told us to let her know if we needed anything and left the room with Dave. Linda sent Dave with Jennifer to familiarize himself with the kitchen where the ice chips were. She wanted to get him out of the room for a minute because he was understandably wired and nervous.

Next, Linda adjusted the temperature in the room. Apparently the temperature was set low so the "heat furnace" moms would be comfortable. Unfortunately, Dave and Linda were complaining that the room was as cold as a meat locker. They whined about being able to see their breath, so I let her turn up the heat. Linda got out some magazines and put my lip balm on the side table, which was incredibly useful. Due to the heavy breathing, my lips got dry and irritated. Dave came back into the room, and I sensed he felt relieved and more confident. He had some sense of control with what he just learned. Having Linda there helped to relieve some of the responsibility and pressure.

It was 8 a.m. Jennifer came in and checked me. I knew the drill. I was still 1 centimeter along, so we settled in for a long day. Linda sat in the rocking chair on my left side reading me the baby's horoscope and chatting about stuff, while Dave pretended to catch a few winks of sleep on the sofa in the lounge part of our room. My contractions resembled menstrual cramps, so they were manageable with the breathing.

At 9 a.m., Linda turned on the TV and we watched "Live With Regis and Kathy Lee." I found it hard to concentrate on what they were saying, but it took my mind off of things. Jennifer came in to check me and then left the room. I was 2 centimeters! If I kept increasing a centimeter an hour, I'd have the baby around 5 p.m. Boy, was I wrong! A few minutes later, Linda told Dave we should start videotaping moments throughout the day. At the time, I didn't think much of it, but once I saw the tape a week later, I was so glad we did it. It was so exciting to relive bits and pieces of that day, since it went so quickly. I didn't realize how much went unnoticed until I saw the tape. Plus, it was something I wanted to share with our families and, more important, show my child one day. Dave took the camcorder out of the bag and showed Linda how to use it. Next, Linda told Dave to turn on the camcorder, record the clock on the wall, point it at me, and narrate our progress. Dave said something like this, "It's 9 a.m., and we're in the labor room at Grant Medical Center. Wendy's water broke at 3:30 a.m., so we came to the hospital. Wendy is 2 centimeters along and Aunt Linda is here to help. Looks like we're going to have a baby today." Then he'd say something like, "Wendy, how are you doing?" I'd give some dorky, grinning response with a nervous giggle and say, "The contractions aren't too bad, and I'm really excited to have our baby. Can't wait to see you baby Beahn." Then Dave would chime in and say, "OK, everybody, Wendy's starting another contraction so we'll come back later." It usually ended with me trying to keep a pleasant face while the contraction grew stronger.

What I learned about settling into our labor room:

- Remember your labor nurse's name and what she looks like.
- Treat your labor nurse like gold, because when you need something, she will bend over backward to help you.
- Have your birth coach:
  - Set out your focal point, breath spray, and lip balm.
  - Find where to get the ice chips.
  - Learn how to read the labor equipment to determine when a contraction is coming. (See page 207 for a complete list of suggested birth coach responsibilities.)
- Make sure your IV is comfortable. If not, tell your nurse.
- Remember: Your labor nurse will not be in your room the whole time.
- Don't forget to take pictures and start video recording.

Chapter 4

Early Labor

The morning went quickly with Jennifer coming in each hour to check my progress. We decided to pull out the camcorder each time after Jennifer came in to see how far along I was. At 10 a.m., I was still 2 centimeters and the contractions transitioned to a stronger menstrual cramp-type pulling sensation. Jennifer said I was not dilating as quickly as she'd like me to be. She suggested I get out of bed, sit in the rocking chair, and start rocking. I remember our Lamaze instructor telling us the rocking chair helps move things along. So, now I had to figure out how to get my big butt out of the bed. I was really comfortable and didn't feel like moving. However, if getting out of the bed meant things would start moving, then my butt was getting up. Remembering to keep the monitoring belt in place and moving with the wires, I transitioned myself to the rocking chair and started rocking. I continued to do my first stage breathing...aahh, heeeee, aahh, heeeee, aahh, heeeee. Once it was over, there was Dave with the camcorder. While smiling, I waved to the camera and said I was still 2 centimeters.

I sat in the rocking chair until 11 a.m., when Jennifer came back in. As I moved back into the bed so she could check me, I was careful not to disrupt the positioning of the monitoring belt. An alarm would sound if the belt lost the signal with the baby's heartbeat. This happened earlier when I shifted positions. Jennifer was immediately in our room and readjusted the belt. After I got in the bed, she checked me again and I was 3 centimeters dilated. "Wahoo! I'm moving along," I thought. Out came the camcorder, as I proudly announced my great news – and then a contraction came. I found myself focusing more on the focal point while doing the breathing and trying not to hold my breath. It really did help me get through each contraction. Dave sat on my right, next to the monitoring equipment, and held my hand as if we were arm wrestling. I was lying on my right side facing him, and when he told me a contraction was coming, I focused on the little red, heart-shaped tag on the Beanie Baby and began my breathing. I found myself glued to his encouragement and searching for those five magical words of relief: "The contraction is going away."

It was getting close to noon and the pain was starting to become more intense. Once the contraction was over, the pain went away, and I was fine. I told myself early on in my pregnancy that I wasn't going to be a superhero and have the baby without drugs. I wanted to focus my attention on the baby being delivered and not the pain I was going through. I'm not afraid to admit that I'm a wimp when it comes to pain. My labor motto, "Pain is not my friend, drugs are." Women who have had natural deliveries must truly be wonder women because I couldn't even imagine enduring the pain I knew was sure to come. I discussed the use of drugs with my doctor when I was eight months pregnant. I told her I didn't want to be loopy from the drugs because I wanted to remember as much as possible. Dr. Morris agreed that early on in the labor, she would allow the nurse to give me something to take the edge off. She said the drug would wear off in an hour or so, and she assured me I would not be incoherent.

It must have been lunchtime when I decided I needed something to take the edge off. The contractions were lasting longer and becoming more intense. The breathing got me through it, but I was running out of patience and getting tired. I was getting to the point where I really wanted to get things moving along, and I found my pleasant, excited, positive attitude slipping away. Jennifer came in for my 12 p.m. progress check. Now that I was eager to get things moving along, these hourly "dilation checks" held new meaning, indicating how much more I had to endure. She noticed my attitude change and quickly checked me and said I was still 3 centimeters.

"Shit, God dammit!" I thought to myself. I told her the pain was starting to be uncomfortable, and I needed something for the edge. As Jennifer left the room, she told me she would check Dr. Morris' verbal orders and bring me something shortly. Before we arrived at the hospital, Dr. Morris provided the nursing staff with instructions regarding the drugs to administer should I ask for them. Shortly after Jennifer left the room, I started to get the shakes. Judy told me this had happened to her, so I didn't panic when it happened to me. My arms and shoulders started to shake uncontrollably. It was like having the chills, but instead of shivering, I would shake. Judy said this was normal and was the body's response to the release of adrenaline. This would continue to happen to me on and off throughout the day. Each time it happened, Dave felt so bad. I knew he wished there was something he could have done.

Once the shakes were over, out came that goddamn camcorder, so I put on my happy face and said no progress. Now, my total focus and attention were on getting through the contractions. I couldn't concern myself with anything else (such as how Dave was holding up), nor could I think about asking for ice chips or shifting my position in the bed. Linda, the saint, kept anticipating my needs, providing me with ice chips and lip balm. Both she and Dave kept up with the encouragement, and I think they knew the rough part was coming.

Jennifer came back shortly after with an IV bag. She announced my drugs were here, and I was so relieved. I asked her if I was getting a shot and she replied, "Your drugs are in the IV bag, so it should take effect pretty quickly."

I remember thinking, "That shot in the hand was worth it if it means I'll feel better soon." Once the IV was connected, I eagerly waited for the drugs to kick in. To my slight disappointment, the pain wasn't gone, but it wasn't as sharp. I thought about the fact that I was only 3 centimeters along and was getting very uncomfortable. I thought I had to wait until I was 6 centimeters before they would give me my epidural. How in the world would I last another 3 centimeters so I could get it, I thought. Just then, I heard Linda tell Dave it was 12:30 p.m., and he should go get some lunch. It never occurred to me that he needed to eat. Dave was probably starving but hadn't said anything because he wanted to help me through the contractions. Linda knew he would wolf down his food and be back in a flash, so she jokingly told him he was not allowed back in the room until 1 p.m. Dave left the room and went to the cafeteria. I think it was a relief for him to get out of the room and take a breather. I was glad Linda was there with me, because I didn't want to be left alone. I didn't notice, but Linda said he was so nervous and uptight and needed some time to "chill out." She realized that he needed a breather and we had a long way to go.

After Dave left, I laid in bed holding Linda's hand talking between contractions, which was comforting. It made me feel less alone in what I was going through. Dave came back at 1 p.m., resulting in the "changing of the guards." Dave took my hand because it was Linda's turn to go down to the cafeteria for a few minutes. As we got ready for the next contraction, I could smell food on his breath. Oh my God! It hit me how hungry I was. I would have handed over the keys to my car if it meant I could have a cheeseburger. I made Dave use the breath spray, because I would have seriously injured him if I had to continue smelling the food on his breath.

The contractions were getting stronger and more frequent. Dave helped me get through them, but I was getting tired. I kept falling asleep between contractions, but I was jolted awake when the next one would hit. As they kept coming, I could feel myself emotionally breaking down. Linda came back into the room, but I hadn't noticed. I remember she and Dave encouraging me to keep breathing as they puffed along with me. As I breathed away, I started to feel lightheaded. I got scared because something wasn't working. What was wrong? Please don't let me faint. Just then, by the grace of God, the contraction ended. I told Dave I got lightheaded and decided to change my breathing from the slow breath to the faster one. When the next contraction started, I began (half breath) hee hee hee, (half breath) hee hee hee, (half breath) hee hee hee... I felt better with this technique, so I stuck with it. When it was over, I fell asleep again, but only for a few minutes. I think Dave and Linda decided not to bring out the camcorder. I don't think I could have produced my happy face.

What I learned while in early labor:

- Don't be afraid to use drugs to help with the discomfort while in labor.

- If you do not want to use drugs, discuss your concerns with your doctor beforehand and agree to a backup plan should you change your mind during labor.

- You may get the shakes. It is your body's response to the release of adrenaline.

- Having an assistant birth coach will give you and the birthing coach additional assistance and company, not to mention flexibility should the birth coach need to leave the room.

Chapter 5

The Epidural

It was close to 2 p.m. when it happened. The drugs wore off, and I was having contractions on top of each other for several minutes. I was tired, hungry, irritated, and wearing out. My hair was flat, makeup off, and my body was stiff from being in bed for several hours. Working through a long contraction, I kept breathing, but Dave didn't say the magical words. I thought, "When is the contraction going away? Why is it still here? Please go away. Stop. It really hurts." I could feel the contraction lessening and strengthen with force. I started to break down and cry, but Dave kept pushing me to keep going until it was over. The monotonous feeling of pain for the last several hours wore on my nerves. I started to cry. As I looked up, I could see Dave's eyes were red and there were tears in his eyes. His face looked hopeless and fearful. Out of the corner of my eye I saw Linda leave the room. Little did I know she was going to get Jennifer. She knew I had had enough.

A few minutes later, Linda and Jennifer came into the room. I was wiping away the tears when I heard Linda say the most wonderful thing I've every heard. She said, "I told Jennifer I think you need an epidural and the anesthesiologist is on her way." I think I heard angels sing from the heavens above. Oh my God, I completely forgot about the epidural. I told Jennifer I wanted one. She quickly checked me and said I was 4 centimeters along. Jeez, is that all? I thought I was more like 6. She said she was going to get the anesthesiologist and would be right back. After hearing this, I had hope, because I knew relief was on the way. "Oh please God, let them come in here quickly. I can't wait for my epidural." I got through the next few contractions knowing I would find relief soon. Ten minutes later, the anesthesiologist came into the room with her cart. I was so relieved but began another contraction. Once it was over, she proceeded.

I was really nervous about getting my epidural because I've heard they are painful. However, my frame of mind changed while "in the trenches," so to speak. At that point, I didn't care if she chopped off my head to relieve the pain – just make it go away – and that's what she did. I had to sit up, swing my legs over the bed, and hunch my back while looking at the floor. Fearful of moving, I remained frozen. Jennifer helped hold me still and coached me through my breathing while the anesthesiologist did her magic – and I do mean magic!

I felt a bee sting prick in the middle of my back and then the area grew warm. Next, I felt more pressure, but it did not hurt. The next thing I knew, they were taping the tube to my back and it was over. I swung my legs back up on the bed and sat there so relieved the process was done. I could feel a warm sensation quickly going down my legs and felt immediate relief. I felt so relieved knowing that the pain would go away, but I didn't realize how quickly that would happen. About one minute later, Jennifer looked at me and said, "Did you feel that?"

"Feel what?" I replied.

"You just had a big contraction and you didn't feel that?"

A big smile came across my face and a sense of peace and relief washed over my body. A wave of excitement built up and I gushed, "No! I didn't feel it! Oh my gosh, Dave, I didn't feel that contraction. Oh my God, the pain is over! I can deal with this. I love my epidural!" Then it dawned on me: A woman must surely have created the epidural, because no man could ever produce something so wonderful and euphoric as this thing they call an epidural. Yes, I could see a man creating the bra, pantyhose, and high heels, but a man could never be so generous and understanding to create the most wonderful thing a laboring pregnant woman could want. I loved my epidural!

Once the epidural kicked in, I became a new person. I was happy, excited, and ready for this baby again. However, I knew epidurals wear off and I wanted to prepare myself for the worst. I thought that if I didn't have the baby by the time the shot wore off, I was out of luck. With a solemn face I asked, "How long will this wonderful thing last?" Bracing myself for the worst, I expected her to say two hours or something like that.

Jennifer looked at me sort of confused and said, "Until your baby is born."

A look of disbelief washed over my face with eyes opened wide as my jaw hit the floor. "Wait, let me get this straight. I will continue to feel no pain until after the baby is born?"

Jennifer said she would continue to administer the medication through my IV. I wouldn't feel the contractions any more.

If my legs hadn't been numb from the epidural, everyone in that room would have seen me leap out of that bed, big belly and all, and dance around the room like I'd just won the lottery. To tell you the truth, I felt like I had! "No more pain, no more pain, I will have no more pain."

The anesthesiologist stayed in the room for about 10 more minutes to monitor the dosage and how I was feeling. I felt tired but great! After the anesthesiologist and Jennifer left the room, Linda told me what happened. She said that when I broke down crying she thought I needed the epidural so she went to find Jennifer. She found Jennifer, told her I was crying from the pain, and said she thought I needed one.

Just then, the anesthesiologist was leaving another labor room, so Jennifer went over and told her I was ready for mine. Just at that moment, another labor nurse said her patient needed one also. The anesthesiologist told the other nurse it was first-come, first-serve, so I got mine first. I could have hugged and kissed Linda for being so proactive and finding Jennifer. (Don't forget to remember what your nurse looks like.)

At that moment, Jennifer became my hero. Every time she came in the room, I told her that. If she hadn't acted so quickly, I would have had to wait another 45 minutes to an hour for my epidural. I'm sure I would have been a raving loon by then. I didn't realize that there was usually just one anesthesiologist on call for all the pregnant women and for surgeries. If a mom needs a C-section, then other laboring moms must wait for their epidural until the anesthesiologist becomes available again. They are administered on a first-come, first-serve basis. This could mean that the anesthesiologist is available, but you have to wait because you are third in line. Realize that when you decide you want your epidural, you may have to wait your turn.

Once the epidural kicked in, I was in the bed for good. I could not feel anything in my left leg, but I could move it around in the bed. My right leg was completely numb and I could not move it at all. It was sort of like when you go to the dentist and they give you a shot of Novocaine. You can pinch and squeeze your bottom lip, but you don't feel it. It was a strange sensation, but I didn't care. As long as I could not feel the contractions I was OK.

I was so tired and could hardly keep my eyes open. Linda turned down the lights in the room and I slept for about two hours. When I woke up, it was around 5 p.m. I was very hungry and thirsty. Linda gave me a cup of ice chips to chew on. It felt so refreshing. Jennifer came in the room for another internal. I was still 4 centimeters. She said my contractions were slowing down, which was a result of the epidural. Judy told me this happened to her, so I wasn't surprised. She left the room and came back in with Pitocin, which is used to speed up the contractions. The Pitocin was administered through the IV.

Jennifer told Dave there were Popsicles in the freezer if I wanted one to suck on. I told Dave I sure as hell wanted one. I needed some kind of taste in my mouth. The ice chips did nothing, nor did the lip balm. I completely forgot I had breath spray in my Lamaze bag. My breath was so bad even I couldn't stand it. A Popsicle would do the trick. Dave left the room in a flash, and I'm sure he moved quicker than Carl Lewis sprinting the 100-meter dash for an Olympic gold medal. I think he just wanted to keep me in a good mood, and if a Popsicle would do that, then he would get one as fast as possible. He came back in the room with a grape Popsicle, and I acted as though he had brought me a diamond and sapphire tiara. I was like a kid in the candy shop. All hail the Popsicle! He handed it to me and I started sucking on it. This was awesome! Nothing had ever tasted so good. The bad thing was that I had not eaten anything in about 22 hours, so I quickly chewed it up and wolfed it down. I wanted another one. Dave wasn't going to argue with me, so he went and retrieved a second one. It was just as good as the first one. I felt so much better.

As I sat in the bed just taking things in, I suddenly was not feeling right. My body became tingly and my stomach was aching. I tried to ignore it, thinking it was from the medicine I was receiving through the IV. Attempting to distract myself, I watched TV and talked to Linda and Dave. As time progressed, my stomach started getting flip-floppy, and

I had a terrible taste in my throat. What was going on? All of the sudden, I felt like I was going to throw up. Linda was sitting next to me, so I told her, "Linda, I think I'm going to throw up." She leaped to her feet and started scouring the room for a trashcan. I proclaimed louder, "I think I'm going to throw up." Dave jumped to his feet and ran to the bathroom to see if there was a small trashcan in there. Chaos broke out. I started to feel my stomach make attempts to purge the intruder that had entered my stomach. Panic started to set in, because I did not want to throw up on myself or all over the bed. Since my legs were like Jell-O, I worried over how we would change the sheets. "It's coming!" I exclaimed. Just then, Jennifer gave Linda a small, plastic trash basket and she ran it over to my side. As if on queue, I puked in the basket. It was purple. Then it dawned on me: "Oh crap, I ate that Popsicle instead of sucking on it."

No wonder our Lamaze teacher told us not to eat or drink anything if we thought we were experiencing labor pains or about to head to the hospital. I was so mad at myself, but I felt better after it all came up.

What I learned about getting an epidural:

- If you feel yourself breaking down emotionally, it may indicate the use of drugs or time for an epidural.

- Don't forget your nurse's name and what she looks like should your birth coach need to find her.

- The physician and patient determine when an epidural is administered. However, the epidural cannot be given too soon or it can cause the baby not to drop into the pelvis.

- Epidurals are administered on a first come, first serve basis. When you want your epidural, realize that you may have to wait your turn.

- Once you get your epidural, you're in bed until the baby is born.

- An epidural tends to slow down the contractions. A drug, such as Pitocin, is administered to speed them up.

- Do not eat or drink anything once you begin labor.

Chapter 6

Back Labor

Jennifer started coming into our room more frequently as she increased the Pitocin to speed up my contractions and monitor my progress. Since I couldn't feel anything, I really didn't know what was going on. At 6 p.m., she checked me and said I was 6 centimeters, but my contractions were erratic and needed to be more regular. It was dinnertime, so Linda and Dave were starving. Linda went down to the cafeteria to eat and then came back up so Dave could leave. There seemed to be more activity in my room, so I could tell Dave was reluctant to go. Linda told him to go make a few "progress report" calls on the cell phone, stop and get dinner, then come back to the room. Again, she told me he needed a few tasks to keep himself busy because he was getting noticeably nervous and worried. It was about this time that I started getting burned out with this whole labor thing. I was tired and hungry and my adrenaline was running on overdrive. I was getting anxious to have all this over with. Plus, I wanted to see my baby.

Dave came back into our labor room, sat down on the couch, and began shoveling food into his mouth. Linda was sitting next to me in the rocking chair. I looked at her and asking in an irritated tone: "What is that smell? It's making me sick." She told me Dave got roast beef and mashed potatoes from the cafeteria and was eating it in the room. For some reason, the smell was really upsetting me. My senses were heightened, and the smell was about to push me over the edge. I told Linda in a bitchy voice: "Tell Dave to get the hell out of here. It's making me sick." She had to tell Dave three times to leave the room with his food. He was so hungry, he tuned everything out and was focused on shoveling food in. He left the room and finished his dinner in the hallway.

At that point, I noticed my labor started to change. I began to feel pain and pressure in the middle of my back. At first I thought the epidural was wearing off, and I felt gypped. I thought there would be no more pain until after the baby was delivered. I told Linda to get Jennifer because it was starting to get very uncomfortable. "Please don't let my wonderful epidural go away," I thought.

The pain began to feel more intense, so I had to go back to the faster breathing: hee hee hee, hee hee hee... It was as if I was having contractions again. Each time my body had a contraction, my back would start to hurt. After a minute or two, it went away. Jennifer came into the room and we talked about the pain. She assured me the epidural was not wearing off. She told me to lie on my side, so I did, while Dave held my hand and offered encouragement. I began to sweat and feel hot. Linda went and got a cold washcloth and wiped my face and neck, which felt good. I was getting scared because I knew the baby was starting to make progress and was beginning to maneuver through my pelvis. I was experiencing what they call back labor. The most common position for the baby during labor is the anterior position, in which the back of the baby's head is toward the mother's abdomen. When the back of the baby's head is against the mother's spine, this is known as posterior position. The posterior position can result in pressure on the mother's back resulting in back labor.[1]

I have heard from my friends that back labor hurts, but this sucked. The pain was in the middle of my back, with immense pressure on my lower back near my tailbone. I was

[1]See page 220 for Bibliography.

lying on my right side holding Dave's hand in the arm wrestling hold, while continuing my breathing. Jennifer told Linda to get on the other side of the bed and use her hands to press on my lower back when the pain started. This did relieve the pain, but I still had to do the breathing. Finding a new focal point, because I was lying on my side, helped keep my concentration on the breathing and getting through each contraction. Oddly enough, I could not feel the contraction, but I could feel a sense of pressure ever so slowly moving lower and lower down toward my crotch.

What I learned about back labor:

- Get the baby off your back. Try changing positions, such as lying on your side, to remove the pressure of the baby from your back.

- Apply heat or cold to your back. Warm or cold compresses may be comforting.

- Apply counter pressure. Your partner may use the heel of his hand or fists to press against the area of greatest discomfort.[2]

---

[2] See page 220 for Bibliography.

Chapter 7

Getting Ready

At 7 p.m., Jennifer came in and announced that she was going to check me for the last time because her shift was over. She told me I was 8 centimeters and moving along very well. I was disappointed that she would not be there until the end, but I knew what it was like when your workday ends and you're ready to get the heck out of there.

Peggy was my next labor nurse and she was so cool. She came into the room and introduced herself. She was about 45 years old, had been a labor nurse for many years, was knowledgeable and confident, and had a funny, spunky personality. Peggy told me she paged Dr. Morris to let her know I was 8 centimeters. She said I was progressing nicely, so she was going to start getting things ready. I think it really hit me that the baby was coming soon. She rolled in a cart filled with various metal instruments, a gown, a plastic face shield for the doctor, towels, and other items for the baby's arrival. Next, she brought out what was called the "French fry warmer." This cart with a bright light was used to warm up the baby once it arrives.

While all this was going on, Linda and Dave kept trading places. One person would hold my hand and breathe with me while the other pressed on my lower back when the pain came. In between, one of them would wipe my forehead and neck with a cold washcloth. During the back labor, I had the strangest sensation I was about to poop. I kept telling Linda and Dave about this feeling. I was actually embarrassed at the thought of me having a bowel movement right there in the labor bed. It was such an odd feeling because the baby was pressing down, but my natural reaction was to try and hold it in, like I actually had control of it. Judy did warn me that during delivery, women could have a bowel movement. But most of the time they don't even know that they have done this. Of course, the nurses are so professional that they never announce this and quickly deal with the situation in a discreet manner.

As the baby made progress, the pain and pressure subsided. Dave was getting anxious, so Linda suggested he take a walk down the hall to get a drink of water. He seemed relieved and left the room for a few minutes. Linda said he had been really nervous and wound very tight for the past two hours, so she suggested here and there that he leave the room and run outside and provide a status call on the cell phone. Most hospitals do not allow the use of cell phones on the premises because the frequency waves from the cell phone interfere with the hospital monitoring equipment.

Throughout the day Dave would run outside and call my mom and his sister, Marsha, who would then call the rest of the family. Getting out of the room did him a lot of good because it helped calm his nerves for a few minutes.

Other things I learned during labor:

- It is possible to have a bowel movement during delivery, but it is handled in a discreet manner so most laboring moms don't even know it happened.
- Many hospitals do not allow the use of cellular phones within the building because the frequency waves interfere with hospital equipment.

Chapter 8

Labor and Delivery

It was 8:15 p.m. and Peggy checked me. I was 9 centimeters and closing in on 10. Peggy said she was going to page Dr. Morris and tell her it was time. I figured Dr. Morris would be here around 8:30 and we would have our baby by 9. At 8:45, Peggy checked me again and she said I was 10 centimeters and we could start pushing once Dr. Morris got there. Next, she removed the bottom portion of the bed at my feet. Peggy then set up the leg stirrups. They were not the foot stirrups that I expected, but rather metal, padded curved supports in which I could rest the back of my knees. They were dish-like and attached to the side of the bed. Since my legs were numb, Peggy hoisted them up into the leg supports. By the time all this was done, Dr. Morris showed up, and I was glad to see her. Her presence meant I could start pushing and the baby would be here soon. All I knew was that I wanted to have this baby. We were going on 18 hours of dealing with all of this and I was ready for it to be over. Plus, I was anxious to find out if it was a boy or girl.

Once Dr. Morris got situated, I was allowed to push. With Linda on my right side and Dave on my left, they proceeded to fold me in half like a taco when the monitor signaled a contraction was starting. When this happened, I took a deep breath, started pushing, and slowly releasing air as they counted to 10. Dr. Morris said she could see the top of the head.

Dave wanted to watch the entire birth, but I was afraid he would be grossed out, get lightheaded or suffer from "crotch shock." I told him earlier that if he fainted, we'd just leave him on the floor. Anyway, Dave looked and was fascinated, but I didn't want to see it. I was afraid of getting really freaked out if I saw strange things happening to my body.

The next thing shocked Dave, Linda, and me. Dr. Morris announced that the baby had red hair. She and Peggy, both red heads, started to cheer. Dave looked at me and said we needed to talk about that, and I laughed. No one in either of our families had red hair. After 25 minutes of pushing, the head came out and then I felt the pressure of a shoulder coming out. It did not hurt at all, but I could feel the release of pressure, which must have been one of the shoulders. All of a sudden, I felt a tugging and a whoosh as the rest of the baby slipped out. I looked at Dave and he said with tears in his eyes, "It's a boy." I pictured him catching a baseball with our son and burst into tears. I don't mean a whimpering sort of cry, I mean a full all-out bawling sort of wailing.

I cried hard for about a minute; I couldn't see anything through the tears. I think it finally hit me that I just had a baby. Yes, I had been carrying this thing around in my belly for the past 9 months, but I was just a word: pregnant. The full realization hit me: I am a mom. Peggy asked what his name was and I proudly announced, Colin Michael Beahn. It was the most beautiful name I had ever heard.

Dr. Morris said he was a big boy. As they cleaned off Colin, Dave cut the umbilical cord and Dr. Morris put Colin on my belly. He didn't cry when he came out or when they placed him on my belly. I looked my baby straight in the eyes and instantly fell in love with him. I can't explain it other than to say a deep connection was made, and, to me, nothing else in the world mattered. Colin's plump, pink, angelic face just stared at me, questioning what just happened. His dark eyes looked at me through swollen slits, while his tiny pink lips were slightly open. He seemed so relieved that it was over. I sang "Happy Birthday" to him as I looked over every inch of his face and body and I ran my hands over his head, arms, legs, and back. He was the most precious gift I ever received, better than any Christmas gift I could have gotten. Forget about any other important accomplishments in my life. They pale in comparison to this.

Dave and I had a few minutes with Colin and then Peggy took him over to the French fry warmer to check him and put on his ID bracelet and leg security tag. In the meantime, Dr. Morris began working on removing the placenta. It was very uncomfortable, but after a few pushes, it was out pretty quick. Once this was done, Dr. Morris and Peggy each held Colin and guessed what his weight was. Peggy said 8 pounds, 3 ounces, and Dr. Morris said 8 pounds, 6 ounces. Dave later came back from the nursery and announced "super chunk" Colin weighed in at 8 pounds, 13.5 ounces and was 20-1/2 inches long. Boy, were they off on their guesses. I can't believe my 5 foot, 1 inch frame gave birth to a baby that weighed nearly 9 pounds. I was stunned!

Next, Peggy put ID bracelets on Dave and me and then helped me breastfeed Colin for the first time. I felt awkward and sort of stupid because my boob was out in full view and I had no idea what I was doing. After a few attempts, he seemed to latch on – or what I thought was latch on – and nursed for a few minutes. I'm not sure if he got anything, but it helped me get used to it. Once he started nursing, it honestly felt like the most natural thing to do, which surprised me. I knew I was going to breastfeed, but I was afraid it would feel creepy. It turned out to be the exact opposite. (I talk about this more in the breastfeeding chapter.) My nursing session lasted for about 10-15 minutes. Dr. Morris said she wanted to take Colin down to the nursery for a thorough check and record the statistics, so Dave and Linda grabbed the camcorder and followed her. I stayed behind to get cleaned up. I was so glad they recorded Colin's experience. Since I saw it later, I felt like I didn't miss out on it and got to see everything. I wanted to soak up as much of this experience as I could.

I didn't realize this until after the fact, but in all the excitement, we forgot to take pictures and use the camcorder after the baby arrived in the delivery room. We were so overwhelmed with joy we forgot to take pictures of us holding the baby. I would later kick myself for not doing either of them. I can honestly say our videotape footage is the most precious thing to me because I can relive the excitement and remember the details.

What I learned about labor and delivery:

- Most times your doctor will arrive for the grand finale, when you push. He or she will stay after the baby is born to deliver the placenta, get you taken care of, and check the baby.

- The ID tags and security band are placed on the baby while still in the labor room. Next, the ID bracelets are put on the mother and father.

- All the statistics, height, weight and length, are commonly gathered in the nursery, not in your labor room.

- If breastfeeding, your first session will occur shortly after birth. Don't be afraid to ask your nurse for help.

- Birth coaches should take pictures and record video! But don't be surprised if the hospital does not allow the actual birth to be recorded, due to liability reasons.

Chapter 9

Having a Baby

After they all left, another nurse came in with the Jell-O, crackers and water I had requested. I wolfed it down. Peggy came in and told me to take a shower. I was kind of scared to get on my feet, but the feeling was back in my legs again, so I lumbered over to the shower with Peggy's help. She had put a shower chair in the stall, so I could sit down and use the handheld sprayer. I was sort of shaky, but it was by far the best shower I've ever taken. It was so hot and long, another nurse checked on me twice to see if I was OK. I reluctantly got out of the shower, dried off, and put on the hospital-issued netting underwear. They surely were not from the Victoria's Secret catalog, but I grew to love them! (I brought home four pair and wore them and washed them out for the first two weeks I was home.) Before I put them on, the nurse told me to put the big diaper-looking pad on the crotch area. After I did that, she took another long, rectangular, puffy pad, bent it in half until it made a snapping sound, straightened it out, and handed it to me. It was a cold, ice pack/pad to put in the crotch part of my underwear. This turned out to be the second most wonderful thing next to the epidural. You would think something cold on your crotch would not be a good thing, but these ice packs felt so good and provided temporary relief. Not only was it cold, it was absorbent. I put on my bulky underwear, the hospital-issued gown, and no-skid socks. I felt so much better.

With Colin in the nursery, Dave and Linda came back into the labor room and got ready to go to our recovery room. A different nurse came in with a wheelchair, so I shuffled over to it and slowly sat down. Dave became our pack mule. He had both of our Lamaze bags, camera and camcorder bags, my street clothes, and the Lamaze pillows, while Linda held her bag. She was heading home, so I thanked her for a stellar performance. She did such a great job helping both Dave and me through this, I felt like we owed her the world. To this day, Dave and I both agree that we don't know what we would have done without her. She truly was our strength during an overwhelming time.

At midnight, the nurse wheeled me through the labor and delivery area and took us to our room. I was so relieved to get into our room and into bed. All I wanted to do was shut my eyes. I was completely drained of all my energy. My crotch was beginning to hurt because I had a severe case of hemorrhoids and an episiotomy. I took the medication the nurse gave me and after awhile felt some relief. Dave had set up his cot, changed into sweat pants, got into bed, and we both closed our eyes, so ready for sleep. Little did we know, sleep would become a foreign concept, a luxury.

What I learned about having a baby:

- The use of drugs during labor does not mean you are a bad mom. Millions of laboring women have relied on them, and their babies are just fine.

- Don't be afraid to ask for help. Communicate your needs with your labor nurse.

- Work together as a team with your labor coach. He feels just as nervous, scared and utterly helpless with your situation.

- Consider having a strong, reliable family member or close friend in the labor room to help provide support for you and your spouse.

- Be realistic about labor. It will be uncomfortable and, at times, painful, but if millions of women can do this, so can you!

- Nothing in the world prepares you for this wonderful, magical experience, so take in every detail and enjoy it!

Once the Baby Arrives

Chapter 10

The First Several Hours

Dave and I decided to keep Colin in the nursery during the night so we could get some sleep. My older sister, Deb, "the pro" with three children, told me to use the hospital to our advantage and keep Colin in the nursery during the night. She said the nurse would bring the baby in every three hours so I could breastfeed him. However, if I wanted to see him at any time, I could press the buzzer and ask the nurse if the baby could be brought down from the nursery. Deb said the bonding would grow naturally, but she suggested I keep the baby in the nursery at night so I could use that time to sleep and recover. This was a valuable piece of advice, because when Colin was in our room, each time he cried, one of us was on our feet to take care of him. She said we wouldn't sleep a wink when he was in our room. She was right.

We got settled in our room and fell asleep around 1:00 a.m. Colin was brought in at 3 a.m. and I had my first breastfeeding "session" alone with him. I adjusted the bed and propped one of my Lamaze pillows behind me, and the other on my lap. The nurse confirmed the numbers on my security bracelet with Colin's band, took him out of the cart, and handed him to me. I was afraid of holding him because he seemed so wobbly and fragile. His head rolled around if I didn't support it properly, and he looked so tiny.

I didn't realize it until later, but the hospital has two types of gowns, standard patient gown and nursing gowns. Make sure you get a nursing hospital gown, because they have two slits in the front. I spent the first 24 hours wrestling in and out of the standard gown each time I had to nurse the baby. One of the nurses finally noticed me struggling and asked why I didn't have a nursing gown. I told her I didn't know they were available. Once I got the nursing gown, things went much better. But that first nursing session in our room was an interesting one.

First, I got my gown undone, boobs exposed, and then the nurse handed Colin to me. I told her this was his first feeding outside of the delivery room and asked her to stay for a few minutes. I wasn't sure what to do next, so I took the bundle and put him to my boob. Colin was more interested in sleeping and I was sort of embarrassed because I didn't know what to do. The nurse stepped in and told me to get him out of the blanket because he was too toasty warm to eat. So I took him out of the blanket and removed his cap. He was wearing a long-sleeve T-shirt and a tiny white diaper. Colin started to wake up after the sudden drop in temperature. Remembering what I had learned in the breast-feeding class, I started with putting his belly to mine and placing his nose to my nipple. (belly-to-belly, nose-to-nipple). Handling him was my biggest problem because I needed three hands. I laid him on his left side to my right breast. Unfortunately, the pillow didn't provide total support, but it helped. Remembering what the breastfeeding instructor said, I placed the nipple near his mouth and started to rub it against his top and lower lip. I was told this would pique his interest and prompt him to open his mouth. Once he opened his mouth (and it only happens for a second so you have to be quick), using my left hand, I quickly pressed his mouth onto my nipple. The objective was to get the baby to open his mouth wide so I could get as much of the areola, the dark part of the nipple area, into his mouth. I didn't know this until the nurse told me, but the nipple must be sucked to the back part of the roof of the baby's mouth. Next, she told me breastfeeding should not be painful. If I was experiencing any kind of pain, it most likely meant the baby was not latched on properly. If that were to happen, she told me to break the seal on the breast by sticking my finger in the side of Colin's mouth and scoop out the nipple. Then I should start over and try to get him to latch on properly. She also told me to rub the underside of his chin if he stopped nursing. This will prompt him to start suckling again. She warned me not to use the breast as a pacifier (letting the baby latch on but not suckle) and the "golden rule": No snacking. The objective is to get the baby to latch on and suckle continuously. If not, he will drink a little bit and then fall asleep, only to wake up an hour later wanting to eat again.

I noticed that Colin started to fall asleep after about 10 sucks. I had to keep rubbing the underside of his chin to get him to continue nursing. After about ten minutes of trying to get him to latch on and continuously suckle, I awkwardly switched him to my left breast and started the procedure again. Most of the time I spent trying to get him latched on. The nursery nurse came back to see how we were doing. She asked me how long he nursed from each breast. I had no idea. I lied and told her 10 minutes. She wrote it down on his chart, scooped up Colin, put him in the baby bin and wheeled him out of the room back to the nursery. I looked at the clock and it said 4:05 a.m. I was so relieved that my first session was over. I thought it went OK, but I had no idea how much he actually drank. I lowered the top part of the bed and turned out the light. I lay there for a few minutes thinking, "I can't believe I have a baby." I closed my eyes and quickly fell asleep.

What I would tell first time moms about the first several hours after the baby arrives:

- Keep the baby in the nursery during the night, so you can get some sleep and recover. Don't let anyone pressure or guilt you into keeping the baby in your room throughout the night.

- If you bottle-feed your baby, wash out and save the hospital nipples from each feeding. Bring them home and use them. Your baby will already be accustomed to the nipples.

- If you are breastfeeding, the nursery room nurses will bring your baby to you every three hours throughout the night.

- If nursing, make sure the nurse gives you a hospital nursing gown. If you aren't given one, ask for one.

- Your first "on-your-own" breastfeeding session may be awkward. Don't be afraid to ask for help. That's what the nurses are there for.

- Take your baby out of the blanket so he wakes up to nurse.

- Remember: belly-to-belly, nose-to-nipple. Rub the nipple on his lips and when he opens his mouth, quickly push his mouth over your nipple. Rub the underside of his chin to keep him suckling.

- If you experience pain during breastfeeding, most likely the baby is not latched on properly. Remove the nipple and try again.

- You may spend a good deal of time trying to get the baby to latch on, but he is learning and will get the hang of it.

- As long as there are dirty diapers, they are receiving fluids.

Chapter 11

Recovery

During the night, a nurse came in the room to take my temperature and blood pressure. My temperature was taken to watch for signs of infection, while my blood pressure was taken to monitor the bleeding from the uterus. I was too tired to wake up, so I just stuck out my arm and opened my mouth. She left after a few minutes and I was ready to fall back asleep. Unfortunately, I was experiencing some pain from the hemorrhoids and needed medication fast to relieve the discomfort. My crotch felt like it was on fire. I reached over to the portable table and grabbed a few bottles containing the medication the nurse gave me. I couldn't remember when I took my last round of medication, and I wasn't even sure what I was supposed to take. I remember the nurse giving me instructions when we came into the room, but I was so preoccupied with the day's events, it went in one ear and out the other. I was really starting to feel uncomfortable, so I woke Dave up and asked him what the nurse told me. He couldn't remember either, so I had to buzz the nurse. She came in and helped me get what I needed. It took about 25 minutes for it to kick in and then I felt so much better. I closed my eyes ready to get more sleep.

What seemed like 15 minutes was actually one hour later. The nurse brought Colin in at 6 a.m. I was surprised to see her in the room again so quickly. She told me the baby eats every three hours from the time I start feeding him, not after he is done. I was stunned. It took me about an hour to nurse him so that meant the baby would be coming back two hours after he left the room. It wasn't that I didn't want to see my baby, but I wondered when in the world I would ever get any sleep. I spent the next hour belly-to-belly, nose-to-nipple trying to get Colin to stay awake, latch on, and nurse. It was equally as awkward as the first time nursing him, but now I had some knowledge and a little bit of experience to build upon. Once the nurse came back in, I lied and said he was on each breast for 15 minutes. She surely had to know that I wasn't telling the truth, but I honestly could not tell how long he nursed. The time went by so quickly and he never nursed a consecutive length of time worth counting. Again, she wrote it down and then took Colin back to the nursery. Just as I got my bed reclined, turned the light off, and rolled over on my side, another nurse came into the room. It was 7:10 a.m.

This nurse was here to check my hemorrhoids and uterus to make sure they both were shrinking properly. She looked at my hemorrhoids and said they were the biggest she had ever seen. I had five of them, each one the size of a grape. Next, she told me to lie on my back, which made my hemorrhoids extremely uncomfortable. I shifted slightly to accommodate her request. Next, she started pressing on my belly, which instantly became uncomfortable. All of the sudden, I felt like I was going to wet the bed. At that moment, she looked at me and said: "I think your bladder is full. You may want to go to the bathroom before we continue."

"Oh what a relief! Oh rats, I have to get out of the bed," I thought. I was afraid to begin this process because I didn't want to experience any more pain. I could feel the tears welling up in my eyes. I was hungry, tired, and in pain from the hemorrhoids and stitches. Then the coaching mechanism stepped in. "You can do this. Just take your time. You'll feel better once you go to the bathroom." I removed the blankets, adjusted the bed to a sitting position and then slowly swung my legs over the side of the bed. Next, I leaned to my left side and slid out of the bed on my left hip, while holding on to the side railing of the bed. With legs slightly bent and weak while hunched over, I lumbered to the bathroom like an old lady.

Once I got to the bathroom, I wasn't sure what to do. I've gone to the bathroom a billion times in my life and here I was afraid to pee. I had experienced enough pain down there and didn't want any more. I switched on the light to the bathroom, turned to the nurse, and with a feeling of complete helplessness, I told her I didn't know what to do. She was so sympathetic and understanding. Her matter-of-fact attitude and casualness to the situation didn't make me feel like a complete idiot. She entered the compact bathroom, held my gown to the side, and helped me pull down the hospital underwear. I was not prepared to see the large amount of blood on the pad. It scared me, so I asked her if that was normal. She said it was and told me to slowly sit down. Of course, my hemorrhoids were on fire. While I peed, the nurse got another jumbo pad for my hospital underwear. To my wonderful surprise, it did not hurt to go to the bathroom. The only discomfort came from my overextended bladder. Next, the nurse put warm water in a squeeze bottle. When I was done, she told me to stand up and squat over the toilet. She showed me how to squirt the warm water on my crotch area, fold over several squares of toilet paper, so it had a flat surface, and blot the area. The warm water felt so good, and I wondered if that's what a bidet felt like. The thought of wiping scared me because I wasn't sure how sensitive the stitches were. But I didn't feel any pain, so I was relieved.

The grand finale came when she picked up an ice pack pad, bent it in half until it made a snapping sound and then handed it to me. I put it in the crotch area of my underwear and then pulled them up. The trumpets blared, the harp began to play and a rainbow appeared to celebrate my new-found personal joy. The cold pack numbed my crotch and took away the discomfort. And to top it off, there was a stack of about 10 ice pack pads sitting on top of the lid to the trashcan. I had an endless supply of heaven right within arm's reach. I was so relieved. The last thing the nurse told me was to put a witch hazel pad on my hemorrhoids. She said witch hazel helps numb the hemorrhoids. I was ready to do anything because these "little bastards," or I should say "big bad boys" were driving me crazy. So, I placed a moist pad over them and hiked up my netting underwear. It felt so good that I actually almost started to cry. I thanked the nurse for helping me and told her how much better I felt. I waddled over to the bed and slowly rolled back in. The nurse checked my uterus and said it was shrinking proper-ly. Just then, my stomach growled and it finally hit me how hungry I was. It was 7:20 a.m., and I felt like I hadn't eaten in days. At that moment, I could have eaten a large pizza all by myself. Before the nurse left, I asked if I could have some crackers to hold me over until breakfast arrived. She left the room and came back with some juice and two packs of gra-ham crackers. I was thrilled. After finishing my snack, I turned out the light and reclined back down to catch a few winks.

What I learned about my hospital stay:

- During my stay, nurses came in my room frequently, so getting rest for an extended period of time was impossible.

- Colin wanted to eat every three hours from the last time I started feeding him, not from the time he finished.

- Peeing for the first time wasn't painful.

- I wasn't prepared for the large amount of blood on the pad. It is natural and will decrease in volume as the days go by.

- Witch hazel medicated pads help numb the hemorrhoids.

- The second most wonderful thing in the world was the ice pack pad. Ask your nurse for them if they don't have any in your room.

- Pack some crackers in your hospital bags to hold you over in between meals.

Chapter 12

Revolving Door

At 8:30 a.m., the door to my room opened and in came my breakfast. Nothing mattered to me more than getting what was on that tray. The attendant placed it on my portable table and left a food menu for me to choose my lunch, dinner, and tomorrow morning's breakfast selections. Dave got out of his cot when he smelled the food, but my fork was positioned for attack should he have even thought about reaching for a piece of toast. I earned that toast and jelly. I think he knew better than to ask for anything. He quickly changed his clothes and ran down to the cafeteria to get his much-needed extra-large cup of coffee. I dove into my breakfast like a wrestler after "weigh in." I devoured every morsel on that tray and actually could have eaten another entire meal.

Next, I looked at the menu the attendant had given me and started making my selections. I carefully circled what I wanted and put it back on the portable table next to my tray. I later learned a very important lesson about the food menu. I was telling my mom how funny it was that I could not get enough to eat. I was laughing as I told her I had eaten a salad, bread with butter, beef tips and egg noodles, applesauce, Jell-O and milk for Wednesday night's dinner. I was still hungry, so I sent Dave down the street to get me a 12-inch Italian sub. I ate the whole sub! My mom asked me why I didn't select more items from the food menu. She explained that the hospital menu wasn't an "either/or" menu. Whatever I circled, they would bring me. If I wanted soup and a salad, I could circle both and they would be on my food tray. I couldn't believe it. I thought I could only pick one of the two choices. Unfortunately, I didn't find out about this option until the evening before we left the hospital. Deb also told me to "save" the fruit, crackers, and juice for those times in between meals when I got hungry. That tip was a lifesaver, as I found my voracious appetite was difficult to satisfy.

It was 9 a.m. Wednesday and time for Colin to eat again. The attendant came back in the room to retrieve my tray and menu selection. Right behind her was the nurse, pushing Colin in his bin. Every time our baby came into the room, I felt a wave of excitement. I couldn't wait to look at his soft, chubby little face and touch his silky, strawberry blonde hair.

The rest of Wednesday involved Dave and I spending time with Colin, eating, sleeping, and forgetting to take my medicine. I realized I needed to take my medicine when I felt an aching, throbbing pain in my crotch area. Why hadn't I remembered when and what to take? Had I already taken my stool softener? Was I taking Percocet or Darvocet for the pain? Why was my brain so cloudy? Looking back, I should have asked the nurse to write down what I was taking and when I should have taken it and kept the information handy for my reference. It would have been so much easier and less painful to simply look at the schedule and know what I needed to take.

That evening, my mom, Deb and Linda came to see us. I was thrilled to show Colin to them, and we had a great time. After they left, I was exhausted. Dave and I watched some TV while I nursed Colin. At 9 p.m., the nurse came in to take Colin back to the nursery. I was sorry to see him go, but I really needed to get some rest. With the nurses coming in every two hours – food delivery and pickup, room cleanup, and flower drop offs – it seemed like we had a revolving door to our room. Getting a chunk of time for sleep was virtually impossible, but I was going to try.

Once Colin went back to the nursery, I fell asleep and slept soundly until the next feeding. Wednesday night went just like Tuesday night with the nurses coming in to take my temperature and blood pressure, and Colin coming in for his regular feeding. The breastfeeding went OK. We had our good sessions and our not-so-good ones. I found that Colin would keep his fist close to his mouth, so I constantly struggled with moving it away, only to have him put it back before I could get the nipple in his mouth. He must have been getting something, because we monitored his diapers and there were results. We were thrilled with the poopie and pee-pee diapers, so I knew he was getting the colostrum from the breastfeeding. Colostrum is fluid suckled from the breast until the mother's milk comes in.

I never thought in my wildest dreams that I would be so proud and excited to see poop in a diaper. But each time Dave changed a diaper, he proudly showed me and I cheered like it was the Super Bowl. To be honest, Dave changed a lot of Colin's diapers early on because I was preoccupied with my discomfort and getting in and out of bed. When Colin needed changed, Dave offered and I gladly accepted his help. I figured since I had to do the breastfeeding, he could take care of the other end. He gladly obliged and I was relieved because I didn't want him to be afraid of the baby.

Other things I learned while at the hospital:

- The food menu selection does not run on the either/or method. Whatever you circle on the menu, they will bring you.

- I saved the fruit, crackers, and juice from my food tray for those times in between meals when I got hungry.

- I should have kept a record of what medicine I was taking and when I last took it. It would have helped control the level of discomfort.

- During the night, a nursery room nurse would bring Colin to me for the breastfeeding sessions and then take him back to the nursery. I kept him in the nursery during the night so I could rest. Don't be pressured into keeping the baby in your room.

- I had some good and bad sessions when breastfeeding, but I had to coach myself to keep with it and believe that it would get easier. I asked the nursery room nurse and the lactation specialist all kinds of questions, and I got lots of tips and suggestions. They are your best resource so don't be afraid to ask them for help!

- While the baby was in our room, we monitored the diapers. Pee and poop was a good thing because it means our baby was eating. Tell the nursery room nurse about the dirty diapers when she comes to get the baby, so she can record it on your baby's chart.

- Encourage your spouse to jump right in and care for the baby. Changing a diaper or bottle-feeding the baby will help him overcome his fears and apprehension about the baby.

Chapter 13

A Lesson Learned

On Thursday morning, Dr. Morris came in after breakfast to check on Colin and perform his circumcision in the nursery. She checked him while chatting with us about his bowel movements and breastfeeding and she answered any questions we had. She noticed Dave was a little hesitant and nervous when picking up the baby. To build his confidence and calm his concerns, she showed him how easy it was to pick Colin up. Dr. Morris simply grabbed the bundled blanket gathered at Colin's chest like it was a handle. Then she picked him up like he was a lunchbox and placed him in Dave's arms. It looked perfectly fine and I wasn't concerned at all – until the next time Dave tried to do that.

Feeling more confident later, Dave changed Colin's diaper and tried Dr. Morris's approach. I watched as he grabbed Colin's undershirt and proceeded to pick him up. Colin's head rolled back with arms and legs spread downward as Dave awkwardly transferred him to his arms. All the while, my mind silently and wildly screamed, "What are you doing!" But Dave immediately realized that something was not right as he looked at me with panicked eyes and a worried face. "That didn't go right, did it?" At that moment, I realized he was just as nervous and afraid of the baby as I was. Something inside me kept me from berating him for what he'd just done. He was already doing that to himself. In a calm voice I said I didn't think that was right, because Dr. Morris had him bundled in a blanket when she did it. I could see Dave mentally beating himself up over this. Then it hit me like a ton of bricks: I just learned a very important lesson. We both needed encouragement and support from each other when dealing with Colin. Being nervous new parents, we were going to make mistakes, but we needed to be positive and encouraging toward each other. It was so important for us to help and encourage each other with Colin's everyday needs. We were a team and needed to act like one.

What I would tell first time moms:

- In most instances, your pediatrician or family doctor performs the circumcision in the nursery. Confirm with your doctor who will be doing the procedure and when.

- Try not to criticize your spouse if he does something wrong or not the way you would do it.

- Be encouraging toward each other when caring for your baby. You want the father to not be afraid of the baby. If he is apprehensive, encourage him to help change or hold the baby.

- Remember: picking at or criticizing the father will cause him to withdraw from caring for the baby, resulting in you having to do everything.

Chapter 14

A Sitz Bath

Colin left the room with Dr. Morris and the nurse for his circumcision. Another nurse entered our room with a towel, washcloth, bar of soap, shampoo, a clean nursing gown and another pair of the hospital underwear. She announced that it was time for me to take a shower. I was so excited because I felt grungy and dirty. My flat hair was plastered to the side of my face and going in several unnatural directions. I had no makeup or lipstick on, resulting in a colorless, pale complexion, and my teeth could have used a good brushing. I slowly got out of bed and went into the second compact room where the nurse had left everything. When I got into the shower, I stood there for about 15 minutes letting the hot water run down my sore, aching body. The pressure from the showerhead felt like mini massaging fingers working out the knots from my neck, back, and shoulders. I forced myself to wash my hair and body and then grudgingly turned off the hot water. After I got dressed, I pulled my makeup bag and blow dryer out of my overnight bag and proceeded to fix myself up. When I was done, I looked and felt so much better. It made a world of difference to feel so fresh and confident, renewing my energy. Dave even commented on how nice I looked, and my spirits soared.

After lunch, one of the nurses came into the room and asked what time we would be leaving that evening. Apparently, standard insurance policies approve a vaginal delivery recovery time of 48 hours from the time the baby is born. A C-section is three to four days, since it is considered surgery. Colin was born at 9:25 Tuesday night, so I had to leave the hospital by 9:25 Thursday night. I started to panic at the thought of going home, not out of fear for caring for Colin without the nursing staff, but out of the high level of pain I had from my episiotomy and hemorrhoids. I told the nurse I would get back to her regarding my departure, and I quickly called Dr. Morris. I told Dr. Morris I was not afraid to leave the hospital because I was ready to go home, but I told her I was still feeling a lot of pain from the hemorrhoids and stitches. That is when I found out that an episiotomy is graded on four levels with four being the worst. Mine was a three because Colin was so big. Add a terrible case of hemorrhoids to that, and you've got a high level of discomfort. I begged and pleaded with her to let me leave Friday. She said she would call the insurance company and see what she could do. About 45 minutes later, Dr. Morris called me back to say the insurance company approved my departure for Friday. I started to cry from the relief of knowing I had a bit more time. I knew that once I got home, I would have to do everything myself. I was so uncomfortable, and I wasn't sure how I would manage. I was sure that if I had one more day to recover, I would be in much better shape. Dr. Morris also told me she would talk to the nurse about having a sitz bath for my hemorrhoids. She said it would help with the swelling and discomfort. I was afraid of having to sit in a bathtub for this sitz bath thing, whatever it was, but I needed relief for these hemorrhoids, so I was willing to try anything.

One hour later, I found out what a sitz bath was, and I have to say that I bumped the ice pack pads to third place. A sitz bath, the second most wonderful thing, is sort of like a mini hot tub for your butt. The nurse entered my room with something that looked like a plastic washbasin with a wide rim. It had two holes, each the size of a gumball, located in the upper backside below the rim. The other part was what looked like an IV bag with a long, clear thin tube. (See p. 58)

4.1 Sitz bath

The nurse lifted the toilet seat lid and settled the basin in the bowl of the toilet with the wide rim resting around the edge. Next, she filled the IV bag with hot water and used a plastic clamp to pinch the tube, preventing the water from escaping. Finally, she threaded the tube through the back hole and pressed the tube into a ridge at the bottom of the plastic bowl. She loosened the clamp and watched as the hot water from the IV bag filled the basin with hot water. Once it was full, she closed the clamp to stop the flow of water. Next, she told me to remove my underwear and pads and sit in the basin. I lowered myself into the hot water. At that moment, if there had been a one-pound box of Godiva milk chocolates next to the sitz bath and I could have only chosen one, I would have opted for the sitz bath. The hot water was more soothing and comforting than any chocolate covered peanut cluster, more inviting and refreshing than any chocolate truffle, and more pleasurable and exhilarating than a mountain of chocolate-covered strawberries. When the water temperature cooled, I removed the clamp and more hot water flowed into the bottom of the basin, pushing the cold water up and out the two top holes in the back. An absolute genius created this! I could have sat there all day!

After my sitz bath, I felt like I could move around more easily, and the pain seemed to subside. The nurse returned to my room, and I told her I felt great, but I was afraid the pain would come back soon. I told her I wished I could receive my medicine every four hours, so I could control the pain. She told me they would put it on the schedule. To my amazement and excitement, my medicine showed up right on time for the rest of my stay. Every four hours, my Darvocet showed up. I figured out that the nurses wouldn't give me the medicine unless I requested it. I had to tell them I wanted the medicine every four hours in order for them to do it. If they say they can't do this, call your doctor and have them request your medicine be administered around the clock. This will ensure your medicine will show up right on schedule throughout your entire stay.

Once I got my medicine on a regular basis, I became a whole new person. I found myself able to get in and out of bed with minimal discomfort. When Colin needed his diaper changed, I happily got out of bed and offered. I am not a big advocate for drugs. Heck, I wouldn't even take Tylenol during my pregnancy. However, I don't believe in torturing myself with pain, resulting in misery. To be quite honest, the drugs got me through a very uncomfortable time. Since I was nursing, I was afraid of what I'd pass through to Colin, but I was more fearful that my discomfort would affect the breast-feeding sessions. In addition, I believed that Dr. Morris would never give me something if she thought it would hurt my baby. Finally, I figured millions of women must have taken this drug to help with the pain so it must be OK.

What I learned for the remainder of my stay:

- Use the hospital to your advantage. Get your rest because once you leave the hospital, you'll be doing everything yourself.

- You have to tell the nurses what you want and need instead of waiting for them to do it. If you are in pain or something doesn't seem right, tell the nurses and let them figure out what is best for your situation. Be proactive instead of reactive like I was.

- If you have hemorrhoids, ask for a sitz bath. It is the most wonderful experience next to the epidural. If you have one, don't forget to take it home.

- Start to prepare yourself to leave the hospital. A vaginal delivery recovery time is typically 48 hours after the birth and three to four days for a C-section. Check with your insurance company.

- Make sure you take your medicine on time. It will help keep the discomfort to a minimum and allow you to focus your attention on more exciting things.

- Don't feel like you are being a bad mom for taking pain medicine while nursing. It's important for you to be comfortable while adjusting to your new role.

Chapter 15

Leaving the Hospital

Friday was the big day for us to go home. I was nervous about leaving the hospital, yet I was ready to go home, sleep in my own bed, and have peace and quiet. I was tired of people constantly coming into our room. We decided to leave after lunch, so we wouldn't have to deal with it once we got home. At 11 a.m., I took a shower, put on my makeup, and got dressed in my street clothes. Even though I had no desire to wear my maternity clothes, I had nothing else. It felt refreshing to be cleaned up and presentable, but it was strange not wearing a hospital gown. I had grown so used to them and really liked not having any clothing clinging to me.

At noon, Colin came in for his feeding with my lunch tray following him. I nursed Colin and then handed him over to Dave so I could eat. It was the best chicken salad I've ever had and nothing was spared on my tray. After I was done eating, it was time to pack my stuff.

I couldn't believe how much had accumulated in our room. We had five flower arrangements, four gift bags, two gift boxes, Judy's breast pump with a bag of parts, my big overnight bag, Dave's overnight bag, two Lamaze pillows, a box of Cheryl's gourmet cookies, my purse, and the camera and camcorder bag. I started putting my makeup, blow dryer, socks, and other items into my overnight bag. Since I took my street clothes out of the bag, I had room to spare. It was a good thing because I was getting ready to "stock up." I was "advised" to take home a few "extras" until we could get to the store to pick up a larger supply of care products. Dave was appalled as he watched me grab the witch hazel pads for my hemorrhoids, five ice pack pads, two bigger pads, the crotch squeeze water bottle, three pair of hospital underwear, my plastic water pitcher, and the sitz bath with the water bag. I was told to take home the sitz bath because the hospital would end up throwing it away. They cost about $45 in the drug store, so the sitz bath went into my bag. Next, I moved over to the baby bin and removed an extra cap, a T-shirt, a blanket, four gauze pads, three packets of Vaseline, three baby bottle nipples, and a few diapers. As I jammed all of this stuff into my bag, Dave teased me about it. "Forget about petty theft, this is grand larceny!"

Once everything was ready, Dave retrieved a cart to load up our stuff to take down to the car. Before he started the process, he picked out a vase of flowers and took it to the nurses' desk. They were so incredibly helpful, supportive, and just plain awesome in every way. Any request we had, they took care of it and were always pleasant when doing so. The buzzer at their desk must ring a thousand times a day, and each time, they were so pleasant and on top of things in a matter of minutes. The maternity staff nurses at Grant Medical Center are top notch and professional in every way. As small a gesture as it was, we truly appreciated everything they did for us.

Dave came back into the room after he told the nurses we would be leaving in one hour. He proceeded to load up the cart with as much as it would hold and then headed downstairs to the car. It took him two trips. I nursed Colin one last time, changed his diaper, and put him in a sleeper Dave had picked out a few weeks earlier. We had a matching hat, but it was so big, it came down past Colin's eyes, so we left on his newborn cap. I placed Colin in a blanket and attempted the "burrito wrap" just like the nurse had shown me. Well OK, the swaddled babe looked nothing like the way the nurses do it, but hey, I was a rookie in training.

Leaving the Hospital

The nurse came into the room with my prescriptions and a few more papers to fill out and sign. After she left, the reality of it all hit me. As silly as this seemed, I couldn't believe the hospital was going to let us take this baby home. We had no clue what we were doing, and they actually were going to just let us walk out the door. I started getting nervous thinking about being on my own without the security of the nurses. I think it started to show, because from that moment on, I would cry at the drop of a hat. I believe that was my way of handling the stress of this new situation. The first time I cried was the first time I wrote Colin's name on the remaining paperwork at the hospital. The form asked for my baby's name and, for the first time, I wrote my son's name: Colin Michael Beahn. The tears came to my eyes and then slowly rolled down my cheeks. I couldn't see the form through the tears, so I had to stop and compose myself. I thought to myself, "I can't believe I'm a mom. I have a son."

Dave came back in the room with the nurse who was pushing a wheelchair. She asked if I had breast pads, and I lied and said no. She left the room to retrieve some and came back with a whole box of disposable ones. I thanked her and then stuffed them into my purse. Next, I slowly lowered myself into the wheelchair and then the nurse placed Colin in my arms. He was sound asleep and looked so peaceful. Dave grabbed the Lamaze pillows and we left our room. I thanked the nurses at the nurses' station, and they thanked us for the flowers. I was so glad Dave did that. We entered the elevator and went down to the main floor and outside to our car, which was waiting at the curb. The sun was shining, and a cool, refreshing, fall breeze was blowing. It felt good to get outside, but it made me anxious to get the baby in the car. I was so glad Dave had installed the car seat three weeks before my due date, because wrestling with the car seat was the last thing our overloaded brains could handle. The nurse settled Colin into the infant carrier in the back of our car and got him all strapped in. I got out of the wheelchair, hugged the nurse, and then lowered myself into the back seat, next to the baby. I used to laugh at moms who sat in the back seat with their kids. I thought it was being anal and overprotective. But, here I was ready to snap anyone in two if they even suggested I sit in the front seat. There was no way I could ride the 16 miles back to our house sitting in the front. What if Colin started to cry and I couldn't reach him? My nerves couldn't chance it. I buckled my seat belt while Dave got in the car and fastened his. We were ready to go.

Dave pulled out of the hospital valet parking area and headed toward downtown Columbus to get to the freeway. I had one eye on Colin and the other eye glued to the road. Colin was sound asleep. Dave maneuvered through city streets and traffic lights, and all the while, my foot was pressed to the floor as if I were controlling the brakes. I thought he was driving too fast and he was so close to the car ahead of us. "What is he doing," my mind screamed as we got on the freeway ramp. "Doesn't he know we have our new son in the car? He's driving like a maniac." I didn't want to be a back-seat driver, so I bit my lip. I decided to look at Colin to take my mind off of Dave's driving. Little did I know, Dave was "white knuckle" driving the whole way home. He later told me he was so mad because he thought everyone on the freeway was cutting him off or driving too close to our car. He said it was the longest, most stressful drive he ever had. When we pulled into our driveway, he said he was so relieved it was over.

What I learned about checking out of the hospital:

- Make sure you fill out all necessary paperwork for the baby before you leave. This includes approval for a hearing test and PKU test. For the PKU test, a few drops of blood are taken from your newborn's heel. This blood is tested for PKU, Hypothyroidism, Galactosemia, Homocystinuria and Sickle Cell Anemia. Your doctor will tell you the results of the test. The birth record for the division of vital statistics also requires that you fill out a form. The hospital will give you instructions for ordering your baby a social security card and birth certificate.

- Make sure you leave the hospital with enough pain medicine to hold you over until your prescriptions can be picked up. Your doctor is responsible for writing or calling in your prescription.

- All moms are required to ride in a wheelchair while holding the baby when leaving the hospital. Enjoy the ride. It will be the last peaceful moment you will have.

- Make sure the baby's going-home outfit is not a gown, so the car seat strap can comfortably snap in between the baby's legs.

- Install your baby's car seat three weeks before your due date. Most local fire and police stations will check it for free to make sure it has been properly installed.

- The drive home will most likely be stressful for you and your spouse. You may want to sit in the back seat and stare at the baby the whole way home. That way, you won't be a back-seat driver, pushing the driver over the edge.

Home Again

Chapter 16

Good To Be Home

It was so good to be home. Dave removed Colin's carrier from the back seat, and we headed into the house through the garage. I could hear our two dogs, Kassie and Willie, barking with excitement! I hadn't seen them in more than three days and couldn't wait to see their wagging tails and smiling faces. I prayed they would love the baby and have a smooth transition with the wonderful addition to our family. They were the "babies" of our family for the past five years. How would they handle this adjustment?

We entered the house and greeted them as we usually do, but they were more interested in what was in Daddy's hands. Dave took Colin into the family room and I followed. A few days earlier, Dave had brought home a blanket and T-shirt Colin wore so they could sniff the scent and get used to the smell. Dave said Willie carried the shirt around in his mouth. I thought that was a good sign. The dogs were wired with energy as Dave put the carrier on the couch and proceeded to take Colin out. He set the empty carrier on the floor and the dogs went crazy. They sniffed every inch of that carrier and then eagerly headed back to Dave. They wanted to see what was in his hands. I was very nervous, because I didn't want them to scare or hurt Colin in their excitement and lack of understanding. Dave let them sniff Colin's legs and feet. Kassie and Willie tripped over each other trying to get close enough to the baby to see what it was. Colin started to stir and they watched him in stunned silence. Dave became angry. The dogs were being too rough and were wound up with too much energy, so we put them in the backyard.

Then we looked at each other as if to say, "Now that we're home, what do we do next?" Since Colin was asleep, we decided to take him up to the nursery and put him to bed. Dave gently put him in the crib, and we left the room. Then it dawned on me. We didn't have the baby monitor set up. I removed the monitor from its package and plugged it into an outlet. Next, I took the receiver downstairs to the kitchen and plugged it in. It started to beep loudly. I wasn't sure what was wrong with it, so I unplugged it and tried it again. It started beeping again. I got mad because I didn't want to mess with it. Why didn't I set this up before we had the baby? Dave and I messed with the A and B channel for about five minutes. Our adrenaline was running high, and we were both impatient. I finally had to walk away because I thought I would cry. Why was this damn thing beeping and what in the hell were we supposed to do to get it to work? Dave pulled out the instructions and got it working. We later noticed the monitor would beep each time we used the cordless phone and the microwave oven.

With that taken care of, we decided to exchange birthing gifts. A few pregnancy books said to get the mom a birthing gift for all the hard work she went through. I had never heard of that, but I showed the paragraph in one of the books to Dave two months earlier, and I told him I wanted diamond earrings. He couldn't wait to give them to me. I sat in his recliner as he handed me a little box wrapped in floral paper with a beautiful, satin yellow bow. When I opened the box, there was a pair of diamond earrings, just as I suspected. They were exactly what I wanted and something that would always remind me of Colin. I told Dave I got him something, too, and I handed over a square box. When he tore off the wrapping paper, his eyes opened wide and he was shocked to see a Ted Williams autographed baseball. He is a huge baseball nut and loves Ted Williams. I joked with him about finding Colin outside one day playing catch with it.

Dave proceeded to unload the car while I stood in the kitchen stunned at the disarray and dirty house we had come home to. There were dirty dishes in the sink, a pile of mail and newspapers on the table, and dog hair everywhere. The answering machine flashed like a three way traffic light, which indicated an endless number of messages. The pile from the car continued to grow, even though I slowly started to put things away. My crotch was on fire from the new level of activity, and I was tired. While Dave was outside, our good friend and neighbor came over to see how things were going. I watched from the window as Dave excitedly told Rick about the baby.

What we learned about coming home:

- I should have asked Dave to come home and straighten up the house before the baby and I came home. He should have brought home a carload of stuff during that trip, so he wouldn't have had to lug everything out the day we left the hospital.

- Coming home was uneventful. I mentally expected the neighbors to be outside with balloons, the high school marching band on the driveway, and the red carpet laid out on the sidewalk, but no one was around.

- We slowly introduced our baby to the pets. They had a lot of energy and were clumsy, but we tried to be patient.

- **New Fathers, please read:** It is common for the father to give the mother a birthing gift. It shows her how much you appreciate the fact that she went through a lot of pain to have your child. If you don't know what to get her, I suggest getting her diamond-studded earrings. You can never go wrong with diamonds. A gesture like this will be appreciated and go a long way.

- Dave manned the answering machine and returned phone calls the first few days while I focused on taking care of the baby and recovering.

Chapter 17

My First Day

At 4:30 p.m., the lights on the monitor came to life, and I heard Colin start to cry. Feeling confident from our last few breastfeeding sessions at the hospital, I brought him downstairs, sat down in Dave's chair and reclined back to begin my first session at home with Colin. With my nursing pillow on my lap, I awkwardly lifted up my maternity top and held it under my chin. Next, I unhooked the flap to my nursing bra and sat there, boob exposed. I laid Colin on the pillow and expertly removed him from the blanket and proceeded with "belly to belly, nose to nipple." I tried to get Colin to latch on, but it wasn't working. I tried three more times. Damn, my shirt kept falling down. I did everything I learned but couldn't get him to latch on. I started to sweat and the shirt fell down again. God dammit! I swore as I finagled the shirt over my head and threw it on the floor. I could feel my face getting red and my crotch was starting to hurt. Again I tried to get Colin to latch on but his fist prevented me from getting the nipple in his mouth. Then Colin started screaming, and I could feel the panic rising inside me. What do I do? Why won't he nurse? Maybe it was the chair. Just then, the dogs started barking like crazy. I'm sure they heard the baby cry. I tried to get out of the recline position, but I couldn't get the footrest to go down. Oh my God, I'm stuck in the chair, I thought. Colin cried harder as I tried to lean forward and press down on the footrest. My mind became overwhelmed with the chaos, and for a split second I thought I was going to cry. Out of desperation, I reached over and pushed the handle forward, and down came the footrest. Next, I took a deep breath, got out of the chair, and took Colin up to his nursery.

I entered the nursery and sat down in my grandma's oak rocking chair. I hauled this thing from apartment to apartment during my single days and just never had the heart to get rid of it. Thank God I didn't. It was quiet in his room, and the chair helped me to sit up straight. I started rocking slowly, which seemed to calm me down more than the baby. Not knowing what else to do, I began singing to Colin and made up the words as I went...

"If you stop screaming, I'll feed you.
If you'll move your hands, I'll open the boobie bar.
If you do this right, you'll be my boobie star..."

I decided to try again to get Colin to latch on, and low and behold, after about four or five tries, he latched on and started nursing. However, he wasn't completely latched on because I felt the nipple slip back and forth with each suck, resulting in a clicking sound. I was so relieved to know he was nursing. There was no way I was going to interrupt him. Click away. I don't mind.

After I nursed Colin, I put him to bed and went downstairs. A few minutes later, my mom arrived after working all day. I knew she was tired, but I was so relieved to see her. At 6 p.m., we all were starved, so Dave ordered pizza again. While we waited for it to arrive, my mom jumped into action. She vacuumed, dusted, did the dishes, placed flower arrangements around the house, wiped up the counters, washed the kitchen floor, and started putting away items from our big pile of stuff from the hospital. After the pizza arrived and we scarfed it down, she attempted to get me organized. Mom took the second changing table I bought at a garage sale, wiped it down and put it in the dining room we never use. (Many of my friends used their Pack 'n Play with the changing table accessory. It works just as well.) Next, she opened the package of newborn diapers and stacked them on the shelf below the changing table. She removed the plastic wrap from the box of wipes and put them on the changing table tray.

The plastic tray attaches to the side of the changing table and holds the box of wipes, so they are close and convenient when you need them. Mom found an old microwave stand and put it next to the changing table and stacked the side snap T-shirts, blankets, burp cloths, and sleepers in separate piles. This made it so easy to reach for things as we needed them. Finally, she put the Diaper Genie and an old wastebasket next to the changing table. The Diaper Genie was for dirty diapers and the wastebasket was my makeshift dirty clothes hamper. I can honestly say that after six months, we used our downstairs changing table 10 times more than the one in Colin's nursery. It was so nice to change him downstairs instead of having to go upstairs each time. Looking at everything she did, I didn't realize how disorganized I really was. I guess I figured that if I bought everything, it meant I was ready, but boy was I wrong. I should have had everything out of the packages and ready before the baby arrived.

I was so grateful for Mom's help, because for some reason, clutter and messiness drove me crazy. Each time I saw a pile of mail or clothes, it made me feel like another thing that was competing for my attention. For the next four weeks, I became very anxious when the house started getting messy and cluttered. Dave and I both made a conscious effort to make sure things were organized or put away, so I didn't feel overwhelmed.

While Mom was visiting, Dave took the opportunity to run a few errands. I was terrified of being at home by myself, so for the next five days, Dave always made sure someone was with me if he needed to run errands. I was so afraid of being alone in the house with the baby. What if something happened to Colin and I didn't know what to do? What if I didn't hear him cry? I just wasn't confident enough to care for him on my own.

Dave went to the pharmacy to get my prescriptions – my lifeline to sanity. I also had him pick up two packs of panty liners with wings, gauze pads for Colin, and some Vaseline. After Colin had his circumcision, the nurse showed us how to drizzle Vaseline on his penis and then place a 3-inch-by-3-inch piece of gauze over it so the scab would not stick to the diaper, causing him discomfort. We did this for the first two weeks we were home.

While talking to my mom, she asked if I had a bowel movement yet. I said no, but wondered when I would. I had not pooped in four days and I was starting to get worried. I was eating like there was no tomorrow, but where was all of the waste going? I had been taking my stool softeners and I ate a bowl of bran cereal at the hospital. Then, the reality of it hit me: When I do have a bowel movement, it is going to hurt because of the stitches and hemorrhoids. I dreaded the thought of more pain "down there." Mom told me to start eating bran and suggested I get some prunes. To be honest, I wasn't overly excited to get this process going.

That night, I was up feeding Colin at 12:30 a.m., 3:30 and 5. After the last feeding, I woke Dave and told him I was at my wits' end and needed a break. I couldn't even think straight because I was so tired and my crotch hurt. Dave took Colin downstairs to the family room, where they cuddled up in his recliner. I went downstairs, took my Darvocet and some Ibuprofen and told Dave to wake me at 8 a.m. I couldn't remember the last time I took my pain medicine, but I figured if I was in pain, I was overdue for it. I decided to sleep in our guest bedroom, where the bed was lower to the ground. Each time I tried to slide out of our big bed, my crotch hurt terribly and I was afraid of pulling the stitches out. My mind was numb and I couldn't wait to lie down.

What I learned on my first day home:

- I had good and bad breastfeeding sessions, but I had to keep reminding myself to be patient, positive, and stick with it.

- Get organized before the baby arrives! I should have set up the changing table (or Pack 'n Play portable crib), monitor and arranged the clothes. Just because I bought everything didn't mean I was ready.

- I didn't want to be left alone with the baby the first several days. Dave always made sure my mom was around if he needed to leave.

- We tried to keep the house clean and uncluttered. It was one less thing we had to deal with.

- I was exhausted due to lack of sleep, but I was surprised to see how well I was adjusting, and I learned to function on low amounts of sleep.

- Recognizing when I was at my wits' end with the baby, I learned to admit when I needed a break.

Chapter 18

Life With a Baby

I was sound asleep when I awoke with a jolt. Daytime light was peaking around the window shade and the warmth from the early morning sun made the room warm and cozy. I felt like I had slept very hard and for a good length of time. What time was it? Why didn't I hear the baby cry? Why didn't Dave wake me up? Oh my God, something must be wrong. I threw back the comforter and rolled out of bed. Waddling out of the room and downstairs to the family room, my mind raced with the terrible thought that Dave fell asleep with Colin in his chair and rolled over on him. I flew into the family room, sure that something was wrong. Just then, Dave looked up at me and said, "We're watching MTV."

I started freaking out. "Why didn't you wake me? I told you to wake me at 8 a.m. and it's 9 a.m. Is Colin OK?" Dave said he thought I could use the extra sleep, so he didn't wake me. Since Colin wasn't crying, he figured he wasn't hungry. I was still mad, and my adrenaline was rushing from the fear and panic I felt from my imagination running wild. I must have had a panicked look on my face, because Dave told me that he could take care of the baby and I was acting like I didn't trust him. I felt terrible and apologized. I went into the kitchen, made a bowl of cereal, and cried while I tried to eat my Raisin Bran.

I couldn't understand why I was so panicky, stressed, and feeling like I could cry at any moment. What was wrong with me? My mind was racing, and all I could do was think about caring for Colin. I wanted to be a good mom, but I had no idea what I was doing. I felt like I was constantly doing something, and there were 10 other things nagging me for attention. My mind felt like a tornado, as things rushed by my eyes, only taking my focus and attention for a few seconds, then it was off to the next thing. If it wasn't Colin or the dogs, it was Dave, or my aching body pulling at my mind and spirit. In addition, I was tired, always hungry, thirsty, and constantly uncomfortable.

After I fed the baby, Dave took him up to his crib and then he went to bed. I let out the dogs, ate a bagel, and then let Kassie and Willie in so I could feed them. I sat at the kitchen table looking at a clean, non-cluttered kitchen. Thanks, Mom. At that point, I decided to search for an old spiral bound notebook I knew was in our filing cabinet. After retrieving it, I started writing. I had so much adrenaline and my mind was racing with the recent events. I thought writing it down would be a good way to get it out of my head. I started to think about my experiences and all the things I learned in the hospital and wanted to write them down. Suddenly it hit me; I could pass this information on to my friends who haven't had a baby yet.

My mom called a little while later and asked how I was doing. I told her my crotch hurt. She suggested I take a piece of paper, tape it to the counter, and write down when I'm taking my Ibuprofen, Darvocet, and stool softeners. She said I needed to take it religiously, because when the pain medicine wore off, it would take the next dose longer to kick in and feel some relief. She told me to write down the time and what medicine I took. I started doing this religiously, and low and behold, I started taking control of the discomfort and pain. Since the schedule was taped to the island in our kitchen, it frequently caught my attention, so I was able to follow my schedule and the clock to take my medicine on time. Why didn't I think of this? Keeping the pain to a minimum helped my spirits and allowed me to focus my attention on other more important tasks.

What I learned once I got home:

- Take your medicine religiously. By keeping a written schedule, you will be able to control the discomfort.

- You may find yourself nervous and uptight once you get home. Give yourself some credit, your life is going through an adjustment.

Chapter 19

Adjusting to Motherhood

I sat at the kitchen table for the next three hours and continued to write like crazy. I was so preoccupied with my thoughts I didn't notice Dave and Colin enter the room until Dave asked what I was doing. I continued to write, not wanting to break my concentration. I said I was writing in a journal the stuff I learned about having a baby, because I was going to write a book. I think Dave must have thought I was crazy, but he didn't let on. During this roller coaster timeframe, when my hormones were all over the place, Dave never made fun of me or criticized me for the silly things I said or did. I was grateful for this because at times I was such a loon even I wondered if I was crazy.

I spent most of Saturday taking care of Colin, eating, keeping myself hydrated with water and catching a few winks of sleep. When I took a nap that afternoon, I slept very hard and never heard a single sound. That's when it started to happen. I began having what I call "anxiety dreams." I dreamt I was nursing the baby in bed. All of a sudden, the baby rolled off my lap toward the middle of the bed and a pillow fell over his body. I sat up in bed and started rummaging through the comforter, blankets, and pillows. I was panicky because I knew the baby was somewhere on the bed, but I couldn't find him. I frantically threw the blankets off the bed and must have been making some noise, because Dave came in and asked what I was doing. I had trouble finding words to tell him I couldn't find the baby in the bed. From what I said, he must have come to that conclusion because he assured me several times that the baby was in his crib in the nursery. I had a few more of these anxiety dreams over the next two days, and each time I woke up frantically looking for the baby in the bed or trying to remember what store I left him in. One of my friends said she thought the anxiety dreams were the body's way of focusing your attention on caring for a baby and becoming in tune with its every need. Dr. Morris told me there was no medical reason for this, but she attributed it to worry, hormones, and adjusting to life with a baby.

Another thing I experienced was the development of my "mommy ears." My good friend Gina, who had her baby two months before me, said early on that I would continually think I heard the baby crying. She was right. For the first few weeks, I would think I heard Colin crying, but when I checked on him, he was sound asleep or lying quietly. I couldn't get it out of my head. Sometimes, I would lie in bed and think I heard him, but most of the time it was a false alarm. I believe this was another way for my subconscious to begin focusing and turning on my motherly instincts. Speaking of motherly instincts, there is one thing I must stop and say: Early on, you may find that you doubt your motherly instincts, but as your confidence grows, you will rely on them. Give yourself credit. If something doesn't seem right, then most times it isn't. You will know your baby better than anyone, so you will be the first one to pick up on any hints that something doesn't seem right. Go with those feelings and rely on them.

On Saturday, Dave was so wonderful and never sat down for a minute. He did the cooking, cleaning, laundry, manned the answering machine, made phone calls, and helped me take care of Colin. Before I knew it, Mom showed up at 5 p.m. and told me to take a shower. I was still in my pajamas and hadn't brushed my teeth yet. Our next-door neighbors, Rick, Lisa and their two kids, were coming over to see the baby, so

I needed to get ready. Relieved to pass the baby to her, I gladly headed upstairs to the privacy and solitude of our bathroom. It became the one room I could be in all by myself without anyone demanding or asking anything of me.

I stood in the shower as the hot water snaked down my tired shoulders, aching arms, and sore back. I closed my eyes and thought of nothing in particular. It felt so good. Not wanting to run out of hot water, I began to wash my hair and body. Then it dawned on me: I hadn't shaved my legs or armpits in about two weeks. How gross. Reaching for a razor, I cut down the "redwood forest" under my arms and proceeded to my legs. That's when I noticed my balance was off. Each time I tried to steady myself on one foot, I had to reach out and lean against the wall. My belly was still about the size of a volleyball, so that was in the way, too. It was just like when I was pregnant. My crotch started to hurt when I tried to lift my leg for more than 10 seconds. Forget it, I thought. I'll have Dave shave my legs. I reluctantly turned off the water and got out of the shower to get ready.

Dave came into the bathroom as I was drying my hair. Afraid the neighbors would see my unsightly legs, I asked him to shave them. If there was one thing that surprised me about Dave, it was his willingness to shave my legs during and after my pregnancy. He grabbed his electric shaver and sat down Indian style on the floor while I leaned against the counter. Placing my foot on his thigh, he proceeded to run the shaver up and down my leg. "Holy cow! I need the weed whacker for these babies!" he joked. Dave's sense of humor came out when he started to tell me how sexy I looked in my hospital underwear. He said my butt with the padding looked like a duck's butt. I couldn't help but laugh.

What I would tell first time moms:

- You may have anxiety dreams, but they will go away in a few days.

- For the first several weeks, your mommy ears will kick in, causing you to think you hear the baby crying when he is not. This also may happen to dads.

- Don't doubt your motherly instincts. You will know your baby better than anyone so do not discount your feelings.

- Don't be embarrassed to ask for help. Family and friends will jump at the chance to do anything for you.

Chapter 20

Compliments, Not Criticism

I was starting to get nervous about visitors, because I was afraid it would be sensory overload. It was all I could do to care for the baby, let alone entertain. I finished my hair, brushed my teeth, and put on my new nursing gown and matching robe. I felt great and looked good. It was so refreshing to be in clean clothes and presentable. Dave assured me he would take care of everything, and all I had to do was take care of the baby. I was so relieved and noticed my mood improve. I was now actually looking forward to their visit. My house was clean – thanks Mom. Dave ordered pizza for the kids – thanks Dave. And I looked and felt good – thank God. The pizza arrived at 6:55 p.m. and our neighbors showed up at 7.

At 8 p.m., I noticed my breasts were starting to ache, and I knew it was time for Colin to nurse. I was having fun, so I put it off for a little while. At 8:45, my whole chest started throbbing, and I knew I was way overdue for the next feeding. Colin wasn't crying, but I needed to get the liquid out before I got a blocked duct. This occurs when there is too much fluid in the breast, and it gets backed up so much that the milk ducts can't open to allow the liquid to flow through down to the nipple. That was my biggest fear with the breastfeeding.

I told our neighbors I needed to feed the baby, so Colin and I headed up to the nursery. I was nervous because the "boobie bar" was packed. Colin couldn't latch on because my breasts were so full. I tried another six times and was unsuccessful. The baby was getting mad and frustrated. I started sweating profusely. Belly-to-belly, nose-to-nipple.

Again, I couldn't get him latched on. My breasts were so full, the areola was tight and flat, making it difficult for Colin to latch on. Trying not to panic, I continued my effort, but I failed each time. We both were getting pissed. Please latch on, please start clicking, I pleaded. Even if I could just get him to start clicking, it would be OK. Eight, nine, ten times I tried. I flattened the areola by pressing my thumb and fore-finger together and got it into Colin's mouth. CLICKING! He's clicking! I didn't move. He nursed for a while.

I was afraid he would get full on my right breast and not nurse on the left one, so I burped him quickly and flipped him over to my aching left breast. His hands were near his mouth, so I pulled them back, but his hand went back to his mouth. I tried about three more times, but, again, my breast was full and he couldn't latch on. Please click again. OK, back to basics: belly-to-belly, nose-to-nipple. I got him on. Please start clicking. If only it would click. CLICK! I froze so as not to disturb what I had worked so hard to achieve.

While I sat there, I heard Dave say good-bye to our neighbors. Next, he and my mom were talking at the front door. She was going home, and Dave was thanking her for everything and telling her to drive safely. Just then, I started to cry. I think the fear and stress of the situation hit me, and I sat there afraid to move, as the tears streamed down my face. I gently wiped my face on my shoulder so I wouldn't disturb Colin and his nursing session. Once Colin was finished nursing, I burped him and put him in his crib.

I headed downstairs to sit in front of the TV and just veg. As I entered the kitchen, Dave was on the telephone. He turned around and once he saw me, a look of panic washed over his face. Since my "crying episodes" had begun, he was always ready for the worst. Seeing the expression on his face, I turned around and went into the bathroom. I could not believe what I saw. Most of my makeup was smeared across the shoulder of my now dirty nursing robe. The gown was wrinkled and stained with foundation from my using it to wipe the sweat from my face, and my hair could not have been any flatter. Oh well, so much for looking good and feeling great.

I went back into the kitchen and filled my water bottle for the tenth time that day. I was afraid that if I didn't drink enough water throughout the day, I would not produce enough milk for Colin. I stood there filling up the cup, thinking about the evening's events and the valuable lesson I learned. That lesson was: Get in tune with your body and don't ignore the signs it gives you. When my breasts were full and I needed to nurse the baby, I should have put that first, above the fun I was having. I paid the price, but I learned a good lesson. After all, I was still a rookie in training.

I went over to our refrigerator and looked at the red, green, blue, orange, and yellow plastic refrigerator magnet letters. When we first got married, I bought a package of the capital and lower case letters so we could arrange endearing messages on our refrigerator to each other. Messages such as "I love you," "hot thing," and "big wanker" turned into joking references such as "farthead Dave" and "Wendy hemorrhoid."

I started scanning the refrigerator for the appropriate letters and began arranging them on the door...

c o m p l i m e n t s   n o t   c r i t i c i s m

I followed these words and lived by them as we continued our journey into parenthood. Every time I looked at the refrigerator, I reminded myself, "compliments not criticism," because we both need a little encouragement and positive reinforcement to deal with the everyday situations we would be faced with.

What I learned about having visitors:

- Everyone will want to come over to see the baby. Keep it simple. If you are going to feed your guests, order food in.

- Make sure your husband takes on all the entertaining responsibilities, because taking care of the baby and getting around will take all of your time and energy.

- Don't ignore the signs your body gives you.

- Compliments not criticism, because everyone needs positive reinforcement during this crazy time.

Chapter 21

Liquid Gold

Saturday night, I was "on duty." I had slept for about an hour when Colin started to fuss at about 1 a.m. I took him downstairs so Dave could sleep. No sense having us both tired the next day. That night, I nursed Colin when he was hungry, and while he slept, I watched TV and wrote in my notebook. Dave would have been mad if he knew I was up writing. He wanted to make sure I was getting enough rest. When I did sleep, I woke up several times drenched in sweat. I don't mean a few drops on my forehead; I'm talking about my hair being wet, water dripping off my face, and the top of my nursing gown drenched. At least I was not surprised when this happened, because Gina told me this had happened to her. She said this was my body's way of releasing extra water I had retained. Dr. Morris told me that blood volume increases when you are pregnant. After the baby arrives, the hormones shift and the body gets rid of the extra water. The first time I woke up drenched in sweat, it scared me because I thought maybe I was sick or there was something really wrong. Then I remembered what Gina said, and I was so glad she told me about this.

At 8 a.m. Sunday, I woke Dave up and announced I was "off duty." I went to the spare bedroom eager for sleep. I had been up most of the night and was ready for some shut-eye. I felt more comfortable sleeping during the day, should I have another one of those anxiety dreams. In my mind, it was more comforting to wake up in a panic, drenched in sweat and rummaging through the bed sheets in daylight, than being in complete darkness. Around the fourth day, the anxiety dreams and sweating went away. Once they were gone, I felt so much better.

Dave brought Colin in the bedroom at 10:30 a.m. for his feeding. I nursed him for about 45 minutes and handed him back to Dave. They left the room and I went back to sleep. At 1 p.m., I woke up in pain and hungry. I went downstairs to eat and take my medicine. My next two nursing sessions, at 1:30 and 4:30, didn't go so well. Colin did not seem to want to latch on and nurse. I assumed he was tired and must not have been hungry, because he didn't protest. He got a little bit of milk, but he didn't latch on and nurse as long as our other sessions. That afternoon, I also started feeling some pressure in the lower part of my belly. It wasn't from the hemorrhoids or stitches. It was the urge to have a bowel movement. I started calling this feeling my "poop contractions" because I would suddenly get the urge to have a bowel movement and then it would go away. Since I hadn't had a bowel movement in six days, I knew it was about time I had one.

Mom came over at 5 p.m. as promised, and she brought Linda with her. I told her my chest was aching because Colin and I had had a few bad nursing sessions. I figured my breasts were full because he didn't drink very much. I noticed that my size 36F nursing bra was starting to "fill up" as my boobs continued to expand. They became very sore, tight and enormous. I tried to nurse Colin to release some of the pressure. After several frustrating attempts to get Colin to latch on, he started to cry. Dave took him from me and walked him around the house to calm him down. I knew my mom was watching me closely the whole time, and at one point she declared, "I think your milk is coming in."

"That can't be," I told her. "I'm sure my milk has already come in. The nurses said it usually comes in between two-five days and it's day six. I'm sure it already came in and I just didn't know it." I told her I thought my boobs were big because we had a few yucky sessions. There was probably extra milk in there because Colin didn't want to drink it. I didn't think it was a big deal. But I stood there questioning why my breasts were getting bigger so quickly. The larger my breasts grew, the more painful they were. I called our good friend, Mary Frances, who is a breastfeeding pro. I told her my situation, and she said my milk was definitely coming in. She told me to get the milk out or I would get backed up, possibly resulting in a blocked duct.

"Oh my God!" I started to panic. I felt like Paul Revere as I ran around the house, "My milk is coming in, my milk is coming in!"

"Where is my breast pump?" I shouted to Dave as I searched through the remains of our hospital pile. Judy lent me her electric breast pump and I took it to the hospital so I could talk to the lactation specialist about it. Included were a bag of parts, but I wasn't sure what they were for. I found the breast pump and bag of parts, so Mom and I headed up to the nursery. I was sweating profusely and was on the verge of crying. I don't want a blocked duct, I thought as I waddled up the stairs. We went into Colin's nursery, and I dumped out the bag of parts on the floor. I thought I'd use the manual pump first because I assumed it would take less time to put together and start using. Not knowing what goes where, I grabbed the white, plastic cylinder with the orange pump handle and my mom handed me a cone shaped piece. I figured that's where I stick my boob because it was an obvious part to the contraption. I tried to screw together both pieces, but it wasn't working, so I tried another circular groove. It worked. Then Mom handed me a bottle, and I screwed it into the first circular area I tried, and that

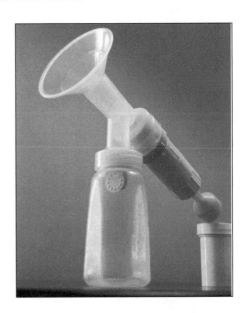

21.1 Manual breast pump

worked. Finally, I slid a small cone-shaped piece in the larger cone and was ready for business. (See picture above.)

Maneuvering my cantaloupe-size breast out of my nursing bra and tugging it through the slit in my nursing gown, I began the process. Remembering what the nurse told me, I placed my nipple in the center of the cone and started pumping. Pump, pump, pump... I watched my nipple stretch farther and farther into the cone. The pressure was not strong enough, so I turned the dial to maximum, since I figured this was an emergency. I pumped about 10 more times and nothing. Oh my God! It wasn't working. My breasts were so large, I thought they were going to explode like a wild fire hose spraying the walls and ceiling of the nursery. Why won't the milk come out? I wondered. I continued to pump while the sweat trickled down the bridge of my nose, fell over the edge, and landed on my lap. Still nothing! I pumped faster as my mom sat on the floor with me offering words of encouragement. "It's not working!" I exclaimed in a panicked frenzy.

Wait! Get in the shower and let the hot water run on your chest, I thought. I remember the breastfeeding teacher telling us to get in the shower. I told my mom I was going to get in the shower to stimulate the milk flow. I stripped off my clothes as I headed to the bathroom. I turned on the shower and waited for the water to warm up. As I stood there, I felt another poop contraction coming, so I headed over to the toilet. The urge to poop had become stronger, and I found myself doing the Lamaze breathing as I could feel my body pushing away the interloper that had stayed too long. I don't remember the Lamaze book saying I'd use the breathing when I had to poop for the first time, but it seemed to help. Of course, I tried to have a bowel movement, but sitting on the toilet made my hemorrhoids hurt, so I adapted to the "football huddle" stance. I could feel the pressure progress lower and lower. Then, all of the sudden it stopped. The urge went away, and I stood there with my breasts still aching and no reward for my efforts.

I got into the steaming hot shower and let the water run down my chest. As our instructor suggested, I tried massaging the milk toward the areola. I could feel the pools of milk that had collected on the sides of my armpits, next to the edge of my breasts and at the top near my collarbone. After about 10 minutes I decided to get back out and try the pump again. I got out of the shower and put on my hospital underwear. Screw the rest of my clothes. My modesty went out the window when I was in the hospital. Besides, I had more important things to do than worry about who was going to see my breasts.

I headed back to the nursery where my mom waited. Just as I sat back down on the floor, Dave came in. His eyes bugged out of the sockets as he excitedly exclaimed, "Good golly, Miss Molly! Can we keep them? Do we get to keep them?"

I have to agree, my breasts were enormous. Now I know why some women get breast implants. Those things could have turned any respectable man into a drooling idiot.

Since the manual pump didn't seem to be working as well as I expected, I decided to pull out "Big Bertha and the double guns." I reached over and grabbed Judy's electric breast pump, pulled out parts, and plugged it in. Once I got it ready and turned on, I placed each cone on my breasts and sat there waiting. Dave fiddled with the levels of suction, and at one point, I felt like my boobs were in a vice. But I was desperate for anything to work. "Please God, let this work. Don't let me get backed up," I begged. Since it was an electric pump, I was sure the milk would start flowing and I'd feel relief in no time. I could not have been more wrong. After about 10 minutes on the machine, I had nothing to show for it – not even one drop.

I had Dave call Judy. "Ask her why no milk is coming out," I yelled from the nursery. Since my breasts were so full, it was harder for the machine to get the milk out. Judy told Dave it would take some time for my body to get used to a machine sucking the milk out of my breasts. As I used the machine more and more, my body would get accustomed to it and start releasing more milk. "Shit!" I said in front of my Mom. "I don't have time for my body to get used to this machine. I've got to get the milk out now." I was getting really pissed, because everything was going wrong, and to top it off, Colin started crying. I knew he was hungry, but I had no milk to give him. Dave went to go get him from Linda. He wanted to see if he could calm him down with a Binky®, the modern word for pacifier.

I turned off the electric pump and started with the manual pump again. After about 15 pumps on my left breast, I saw through the clear plastic cone a drop of milk form on my nipple. I continued to pump out of fear of what would happen if I stopped. Plus, I had to get something out for Colin. The poor kid was getting hungry, and it was up to me to feed him. Even though I had a backup can of formula in the pantry, for some reason, I never thought to use it.

After five minutes of pumping on my left breast, I had half an ounce to show for my hard work. My arms were aching and I was sweating up a storm. That's when my mom jumped in to help. I think this is one of those moments I will never forget for the rest of my life. I'm sitting on the floor in Colin's nursery, wearing only the padding and hospital underwear while my mom is kneeling in front of me holding the manual pump and pumping my breasts.

After 10 more minutes on the right breast with the manual pump, I had 1 ounce to pass to Dave, who started feeding Colin. I worried about nipple confusion, since Dave was using a bottle, but I had no choice. Colin needed to eat, and my boobs were too full for him to latch on. With another bottle attached to the pump, my mom and I spent the next hour and a half taking turns pumping both breasts and passing the milk to Dave. At one point, I looked at my mom and deadpanned, "So, what are you going to do at work tomorrow?" We couldn't help but laugh until the tears came to our eyes, all the while pumping away.

At 9 p.m. my Mom and Linda went home and Colin was sound asleep in his crib. I decided to use Big Bertha to see if I could get more milk. The next two hours were spent connected to the electric breast pump, in which I got 4 more ounces. I was thrilled and I worked so hard for it. Having never seen breast milk before, I marveled at the fact that it looked just like skim milk. Holding the bottle up to the light, it appeared to be white in color, but its consistency seemed to be more watery, like skim milk. I showed Dave what I produced and offered these words of warning: "This is 'liquid gold' and I've worked really hard to get every drop. Please handle my breast milk like you are working with dynamite. Treat my liquid gold with care."

Next, I poured the liquid gold into a locking sandwich bag, put it in a one-gallon freezer bag, and placed it in the freezer. Gina advised me to freeze every drop I pumped, no matter the amount. She told me to build up an extra supply, should I need it. Little did I know my meager supply would be used within hours.

Chapter 22

Breast or Bottle?

Breastfeeding was a huge decision for me because I had reservations. The thought of having a baby suck on my breasts sort of creeped me out. OK, I'll be honest: I viewed my breasts as sexual objects and any activity with them was pleasure to me. Now, here I had to consider an innocent baby who would depend on them for survival. It was hard for me to imagine my breasts as a functioning tool rather than objects of sexual pleasure.

After reading all the benefits of breastfeeding and hearing my mom beg me to do it, I decided to give it a try. In the thirty-fourth week of my pregnancy, I attended a breastfeeding class provided by one of the hospitals. It was a two-hour class and cost $35. Before leaving for the class, Dave begged me not to make him go. Realizing that he would probably be fidgety and whine the entire time, I told him he didn't have to. I was actually relieved he wasn't there, because out of the 30 people there, only four were men, and they looked like they would rather have been kicked in the crotch than sit through the class.

I was hoping to go to this class to learn the secret to successful breastfeeding, but what I got out of it was far better. Through this class, I became comfortable with the idea of having a baby nurse from me. I began to overcome the mental awkwardness associated with first time experiences. As I sat there taking notes and watching a video of several mothers demonstrating how to get a baby to latch on, it did not seem so strange. Seeing our instructor so casual and relaxed about the subject helped me loosen up and think that maybe breastfeeding wasn't so unusual. As I sat among

25 other very pregnant moms who planned to breastfeed, it made me realize that I wasn't alone. If they could do it, so could I.

Four weeks after Gina had her baby, she called to give me the scoop on breastfeeding. The No. 1, most important piece of advice she had was: "Give it three weeks. I don't know what it is about that time frame, but if you can make it three weeks, you'll be OK." So, I burned it into my brain that I had to make it three weeks. I would not allow myself to give up any sooner.

When the big moment presented itself, I was not sure what to expect. We were in the delivery room and the nurse announced it was time for Colin to breastfeed. Taking a deep breath, I lowered my nursing gown top and awkwardly maneuvered Colin to my breast. Thank God the nurse was right there, and after a few attempts, we got him latched on. I sat there completely amazed as I watched my new baby nurse from me. Surprisingly enough, the very thing that I thought would be so creepy actually felt like the most natural thing to do. To my surprise and relief, breastfeeding ended up being the most rewarding experience. There were many times during my nursing sessions when I would cuddle alone with Colin and stare at his beautiful, strawberry blonde hair and search over every square inch of his face, ears, and neck. I found this one-on-one time to be very personal and special because it was something only I could do for our baby. Breastfeeding was something for me and only me to experience and keep in my heart. There was something about him rooting for my breast while being held by others that made me feel needed and depended upon. Knowing that my baby relied on me and needed me always made me feel so good. I loved being the provider and giving the best to my baby that I could give.

When Colin nursed, I honestly couldn't feel any sucking sensation. When he would latch on improperly, I could definitely feel it, but that didn't happen very often. The early days and weeks were frustrating at times, but Gina was right, when I got to the three-week mark, things seemed much easier, and Colin turned into a breastfeeding pro. Once we both got the hang of it, I grew to love breastfeeding and was so glad I did it. Many of the pregnancy books list the features and benefits of breastfeeding, but a few really stuck out through my own experience. They were:

1. **Convenience:** You can go anywhere, any time, and you've got your portable refrigerator with you. No mixing bottles, keeping it chilled, or trying to figure out how to heat it up. You simply go into a restroom, your car, or nursing station and you're ready to nurse. In the middle of the night, it's also convenient because you don't have to mix and heat a bottle while the baby is crying. You simply get the baby, sit down, pull out your breast, and viola!

2. **Cost:** Breast milk is free, and formula is expensive. At $10 a can, which lasts about 3 days, you can easily use two cans a week ($20 a week). The cost quickly adds up as you buy 8-10 cans a month. ($100 a month). While working, my milk supply decreased, so we supplemented with formula. Then at five months, we switched completely over to formula. What a shock it was to fork out $100 a month. (Add $50 for diapers and $10 a month for wipes and it quickly adds up.)

3. **Constipation:** I was told that breastfed babies typically don't get constipated, because breast milk contains a natural laxative. Once in a great while, Colin would get constipated, and it was stressful hearing him

strain and grunt and be grumpy while he tried to work it out. But most of the time, he was my "super-duper-power-pooper" and I believed it was because of the breast milk.

4. **Antibodies:** It was reassuring to know that I was passing on my antibodies through the breast milk to Colin so his body could fight infection and disease. I dreaded the thought of him being sick and this made me feel like I was helping build his immune system.

5. **Losing weight:** Because breastfeeding burns calories, I knew part of my weight loss was due to the breast-feeding. Anything to help that cause was worth it.

Through my five months of breastfeeding, I learned so much. Here are some of the highlights:

1. Teach your baby to nurse until he is full. Once latched on, he should eat until he is full. Don't use your breast as a pacifier or for snacking.

2. While nursing, listen for small gulping sounds. That way you know the baby is drinking.

3. Don't touch or brush the baby's cheeks while he is latched on; babies move their mouths toward touch.

4. Avoid rocking your baby while nursing; it most likely will put him to sleep.

5. Don't forget to nurse equally from both breasts to keep your supply up with both of them. If you experience problems with one breast, you can always rely on the other.

6. Your baby will become a more efficient eater, nursing from 45 minutes down to 10 or 15 minutes each session.

7. Stick with the breastfeeding for three weeks before giving up. It may be frustrating and tiresome, but you will be so glad you did it.

8. If you are going back to work and don't want to pump, it's better to breastfeed for the first four, six, eight, or twelve weeks of your baby's life than not at all.

What would I tell first time moms about breastfeeding? Stick with it! At first, breastfeeding is a lot of work, but it does get easier. You may have good and bad sessions, but know that as each day goes by, you and your baby will become more comfortable.

Should you experience some troubles with breastfeeding, contact your local hospital or childbirth preparation class to see if they have an established network of women who can provide help and support. One well-known group is Le Leche League, a non-profit organization that helps mothers with breastfeeding through mother-to-mother support, encouragement, information, and education, and to promote a better understanding of breastfeeding.

Additional information can be found on the Internet at **http://www.lalecheleague.org/** or check your local telephone listings.

If you are concerned about going back to work, know that breastfeeding is not an all-or-nothing issue. After a month at work, I started supplementing Colin's bottles with formula. I ended up nursing him before going to work, when I got home, and during nighttime feedings. Your body will adjust and produce to the schedule you set. So, if you want to continue nursing, you can supplement during the day with formula and still breastfeed at night.

Know that breastfeeding is a personal choice. If you really don't want to do it, don't. You won't enjoy it, and the stress from feeling forced to do it may make it more difficult on you. If you are undecided or think you may want to do it, give it a try. Tell yourself you will give it three weeks and then decide what you want to do. I encourage you to try it, because you may be pleasantly surprised at how much you enjoy breastfeeding. If you definitely know you want to breastfeed, you will love it! The personal feeling of accomplishment is powerful and rewarding, giving you bragging rights at mastering such a difficult feat.

Other things I experienced while breastfeeding:

- At first, my nipples and areola were sore and dry, and the skin was cracked from frequent feedings. I used the Lansinoh breast cream after each feeding to add back the needed moisture. After a week, the skin toughened up and the problem went away.

- My experienced sister Deb told me to always start my next breastfeeding session on the opposite breast from the last session. If I started on the right breast at 3 p.m., then at 6 p.m., I would start on the left breast. This ensures that the baby doesn't develop a preference for one breast, causing the other to decrease in the volume of milk produced.

- Make sure to burp the baby before switching to the other breast and after he is finished. If the air doesn't get out, it processes through his body as gas and may make the baby irritable and crabby.

- Dave started feeding Colin a bottle at three weeks to give me some freedom. At times, I felt like the baby was hanging on me constantly, so it gave me a break and allowed me to leave the house for more than two or three hours at a time. Even though it was extra work, pumping helped Colin grow used to drinking from a bottle. I've heard that some babies refuse a bottle after months of strictly nursing.

- Colin would sometimes get lazy with nursing after he had a bottle. A bottle doesn't require as much sucking as the breast does. But he quickly learned how to handle both.

- Gina said to pump a bottle after you nurse. Nurse, burp the baby, put him to bed or place him under the activity gym, then use the pump.

- Gina told me to watch what I eat. Spicy foods and vegetables such as broccoli and cabbage can affect your baby. Foods and drinks with caffeine also can be passed to your baby, possibly making it difficult for him to sleep.

- Breastfeeding became easier as time went on. Colin became more efficient and the whole process took less time.

- Mom kept reminding me to drink water to keep my milk supply up!

What I learned about pumping milk:

- Electric breast pumps can be rented through a network of mothers who purchased the pumps. Contact your local hospital's education department or breastfeeding organizations for additional information. The pumps usually rent for around $25 a month.

- My body began to adjust to a machine expressing milk from my breasts, and I discovered that I could pump 6 to 8 ounces of milk at a time. I went from pumping 3 ounces in two hours to 8 ounces in 25 minutes. As your body adjusts, it gets much easier, so stick with it!

- I found that I needed to lean forward slightly when pumping, so the milk would flow down the chute into the bottle. At first, I thought I would lean back in the recliner and let the pump do its business. After 30 minutes, I realized that milk was running down my belly and getting me all wet.

- When bubbles form on the valve, it usually means your breast is empty and there is no more milk to pump.

- Consider building up a frozen supply of breast milk for day care or to keep on hand. If you get sick, your milk supply can decrease, or if you are late getting home, your spouse can pull from the frozen supply.

  - To use, simply take a frozen bag of milk and put it in a bowl of hot water. After it thaws, pour the milk into a bottle, and heat up the bottle.

  - Breast milk can stay frozen for three to six months and can be refrigerated for 72 hours. After 48 hours, I found it to be clumpy and just plain gross looking. I tried to use mine within 48 hours.

- I forced myself to wash out the parts after I was done pumping. The worst thing is cleaning out the parts when your boobs are aching because you need to pump.

- Purchasing a nursing gown was well worth the money I spent. Getting up in the middle of the night and wrestling with my shirt was the last thing I wanted to deal with. I liked the convenience it provided. I also bought two nursing tops, which proved quite useful when outside the house. My friends were surprised when I showed them it was a nursing top, because the stylish shirt discretely hid the nursing slits.

- As a modest person, it was difficult for me to expose my breasts to nurse, but after a few weeks, I didn't even care. It's funny how my modesty went out the window after I had Colin.

- Don't be afraid to use formula if you're in a pinch or need the convenience. Check with your doctor to see what type he or she recommends.

Chapter 23

The Apocalypse

While sitting in the family room pumping milk, I told Dave I had not had a bowel movement in six days, and over those days, I had eaten like a fiend. I couldn't stuff enough food into my mouth. My appetite was insatiable. Mom told me earlier that she was concerned with the amount of pizza (cheese is binding) I had eaten. I have to admit that my eating habits were bad those past six days as I chowed down on an Italian sub, chicken parmigiana sub and pizza, pizza, and more pizza. When I looked back on what I had eaten, there was virtually no roughage, so it was understandable why I was so backed up. To put it in layman's terms, I was literally full of shit.

While sitting there, I felt another poop contraction, so I headed to the downstairs bathroom. I stood in the football stance and did my breathing, hoping for any kind of positive result. Dave came to the bathroom door and asked if I was OK. I was so tuned into my experience that I could only get out the words, "Go away." I needed the time to focus on what I was doing and to get through the contraction. It was just like being in labor. I couldn't deal with anything else other than what I was going through. After about 15 minutes, I emerged from the bathroom feeling frustrated and scared. I had been having these poop contractions all day and they were starting to wear on me.

I decided to go upstairs and take a shower, hoping the hot water would help me relax during this stressful time. I knew pooping would be difficult, but I had no idea it would be so uncomfortable.

I spent the next hour in our master bathroom, hunched over the toilet, lying on the floor, or standing in the hot shower. The hot water made me feel better, but still nothing was coming out. The pain was getting more intense and harder to deal with, and I was getting very tired. The day's events were sapping my energy and pulling at my nerves. After awhile, I decided to go into the spare bedroom and lie down on the bed. I was desperate for sleep, and I was looking for any way to escape the pain. I was hoping fatigue would override the discomfort and provide temporarily relief.

It was 12:30 a.m., and I was in the guest bedroom lying on the bed with the light on. I was coaching myself through each contraction, which began to occur more frequently. I kept myself from the breaking point only by my coaching mechanism, which was growing weary. At one point, I started to cry. The tears poured down my face as I openly sobbed out of helplessness, exhaustion, and fear.

That's when I heard Colin. It was time for him to eat. I became mad at him for pulling at me during a time when I could not even deal with myself. Then the guilt followed. "How could you think like that?" What kind of mother are you?" I berated myself. Just then, another contraction hit, and I started crying. I was overwhelmed by the chaos. Dave brought Colin into the room, expecting me to feed him while my body was dealing with its own personal hell. I looked at Dave as I wailed in pain and tears streamed down my face. I turned into a raving loon as I told Dave I could not deal with the baby right now. I openly bawled and pleaded with him: "I need an epidural. I need an epidural." I was convinced an epidural would numb my lower half, giving me the relief my body and mind desperately needed. Dave later told me that he stood there feeling like it was the apocalypse, the end of the world, as Colin and I both wailed and there was nothing he could do.

A part of me tried to take back control of the situation. I told Dave to get the car seat because we were going back to the hospital so I could get an enema. As crazy as it seemed, I was convinced that was what I needed. It wasn't what I wanted to experience, but I was convinced it would make me feel better. I was desperate. But Dave convinced me to hold off while he called our doctor's office. He bargained with me to nurse Colin while he made the call. Sure I would get the confirmation to carry out my plan, I took Colin and nursed him between the contractions.

Dave called out from our bedroom, saying he left our telephone number with the answering service. He said he was waiting for the on-call doctor to call back. I had nursed Colin for about 10 minutes when the phone rang. I strained my ears, trying to catch any words of encouragement. After a few minutes, Dave slowly walked in the room to face the firing squad. In a calm voice, he said: "I don't think I'm going to tell you what you want to hear. The doctor on call said there was nothing they could do. You're going to have to just deal with it." He slowly turned around, walked out of the room, and shut the door. I felt like the wind was knocked out of me. The reality of my situation hit me hard. There was nothing I could do, either. I cried softly as I continued to nurse Colin.

I'm not sure how I got through the night, but I think fatigue took over, and I slept between feedings. At 7 a.m. Monday, I called my mom before she left for work, asking her to bring me a big container of prunes. She showed up at 8:30 a.m. with two boxes of what would become my best friends. I ate 15 prunes, determined to get this part over with. About 2:30 that afternoon, I could feel the prunes hard at work, so I went back to the bathroom. That afternoon, I lay on the bathroom rugs, covered in a big beach towel, wearing nothing but my hospital underwear. If I got the urge, I went to the toilet but was always disappointed. A hot shower proved to be quite relaxing and comforting, so I spent a good deal of time standing in front of the shower-head. Dave fed Colin from my "reserve," and I used my manual pump when my breasts were full. I would call out to Dave, who would bring me a clean bottle, take my milk, and put it in the refrigerator. Dave used the breast milk so quickly; he didn't bother freezing it.

About 5:30 p.m., I fell asleep on the bathroom floor, surrounded by my arsenal of tools: prunes, breast pump, pain medicine, notebook, pen, and a glass of water. I think it was around 6:30 when I was jolted awake for the finale. I'll spare the details, but after a long 24 hours, I finally had my first bowel movement. It was uncomfortable. After it was over, I felt like I had run a marathon. I was mentally and physically exhausted, but it was a good feeling to know it was over. Thereafter, each time I had a bowel movement, the pain seemed to lessen considerably. After another day, it was no problem, and I was feeling like a champ. I survived another hurdle.

If there were one piece of advice I would give my girl-friends, it would be this:

Once you have your baby, there are two things you need to be aware of, focused on, and ready for:

1. your milk coming in (whether you are breastfeeding or not);
2. pooping for the first time.

While I was pregnant, I quizzed several of my friends. "How will I know when my milk comes in?" I asked. Their reply was always, "You'll know." When I asked how, they said, "You'll just know." Well, let me tell you, unless my tongue turned green or my hair caught on fire, there was no way I would have known that my milk was coming in. However, here's what I gathered from my own experience:

- My milk came in six days after Colin was born, but I remember the nurse telling me it usually comes in from two-five days after giving birth.
- Colin started having a difficult time staying latched on while nursing.
- My breasts started aching and felt very heavy.
- I noticed my breasts grew to an astounding size, and it happened in just a few hours.
- Pools of milk that felt like hard lumps the size of a nickel formed next to my armpits and the top of my breasts.

If you choose to breastfeed, remember that your baby is your best breast pump. However, you should become familiar with the manual and/or electric pump, so you are not scrambling around trying to read directions or figure out how to use them while your stress level is high. Ask the lactation specialist at the hospital to show you how to use your breast pump.

If you are going to use formula, you will need to dry up your milk supply. I would recommend talking to your doctor about ways to do this, and you should be prepared and ready to take action when it occurs.

When we have baby No. 2, I will handle pooping for the first time much differently. In my opinion, I handled that whole situation the wrong way. Not eating enough roughage was my downfall. Next time, I will take stool softeners religiously, start eating prunes the next day, and avoid binding foods, such as bread, cheese, and pizza. Instead of ordering a sub or pizza, my order will include a big garden salad, fruits, vegetables, and bran cereal. Knowing what I know now, my motto will be "the sooner it occurs, the better." Being aware of this process and taking the right steps will give me more control in getting over this hurdle in a quicker, more positive manner.

Life With Colin

Chapter 24

The First Four Weeks

Once I made it over those two major hurdles, I began to settle into life with Colin. It was such a big adjustment to go from caring only for myself to caring for an additional human being who was completely dependent on me. Of course, there were no owner's manuals and I couldn't cheat and take out the batteries. I just had to deal with what came at me and make the best of it. I found that particularly difficult, because I am very much an organizer, planner, schedule-type person. Before Colin was born, my lifestyle revolved around a schedule and planning what needed to get done. I worked, took care of the dogs, organized my social life, and even planned cooking, housework, and grocery shopping. I was comfortable with my routine and liked it.

Suddenly, I found myself at home when I'm normally at work. I couldn't find the time to do simple things like eat, brush my teeth, or change my clothes. Worse for me, I could not even plan five minutes ahead of where I was. My mind was consumed with questions such as: Why was the baby crying when he should be asleep? Why did he only eat a little bit and then fall back asleep? Should I feed him in one hour or hold him off for another three hours? It's situations like this that drove me crazy. I could not gain any order or control, let alone know what I was supposed to do next. My frame of mind was shifting from predictability to spontaneity, and it was driving me crazy.

I decided to call Deb and ask her when Colin would be on some sort of schedule. She said not for a while, because he was only 7 days old. She suggested I write down when I start feeding Colin and when he finishes. This way I'll be able to anticipate when he will need to be fed next and determine if he's becoming a more efficient eater. For example, she said, if he eats at 3 p.m., then the next scheduled time to eat was 6. If he woke up at 5:30, she said, then try wasting time by changing his diaper and playing with him. Should he throw a fit, then feed him, but try to get him as close to 6 as possible. If he was supposed to eat at 6 p.m., but he's asleep, wake him up and feed him.

Deb said to continue feeding him every three hours until I got to about 11 p.m. or midnight. At that point, she said, make sure he eats as much as possible, burp him, and let him sleep until he wakes up on his own. For example, if I fed him at midnight and he's still asleep at 4 a.m., just let him sleep until he wakes up crying. She said you should never wake a sleeping baby at night. I interpreted night to mean 11 p.m. to 5 a.m. Colin always woke up after three hours, but there was hope three weeks away, when he would start sleeping from 11 p.m. to 3 a.m. Four hours doesn't seem like a lot, but adding one hour onto my normal three hours of sleep made a world of difference.

Deb's tip proved to be a lifesaver, because it helped me gain some control and predictability in my new unfamiliar world. Recording the length of Colin's feedings helped me make sure he was actually nursing and not snacking. If Colin typically nursed for 40 minutes, then I knew his belly was full. If he was eating every hour or hour and a half, it usually was because I let him fall back to sleep after 20 minutes, resulting in a half-full belly. It also helped me to recognize the beginning of a pattern, a schedule I so desperately wanted. I had to record the feedings religiously in order to see when he was eating. Even at 3 a.m., when I was exhausted, I forced myself to take the time to write down when I fed him. My mom told me to wear my watch constantly so I would always know what time it was. That was key, because not only was I keeping track of the feedings, I also was still taking my medicine.

My body was still trying to recover from the battle it went through just seven days before. I was not prepared for the bleeding that came after having the baby. Dr. Morris told me that as the uterus shrinks in size, it cuts off blood vessels, which lessens the bleeding. This may result in one week of heavy bleeding, with light bleeding for up to six weeks. My bleeding lingered for four weeks, and I ended up using three boxes of sanitary pads with wings, which were a godsend and a must-have! The day I came home from the hospital, my mom told me to avoid using the stairs and keep my activity to a minimum. She said that too much activity could irritate my stitches and my lower body, causing more bleeding. Heeding my mom's advice, I only allowed myself to go upstairs twice a day. Dave took over cooking, cleaning, laundry, and grocery shopping. I was so grateful for his help because it was all I could do to take care of Colin and myself. Not only was I physically trying to recover, but I also was going through a mental adjustment.

Point blank, my hormones were totally out of control. I was not prepared for the emotional roller coaster I was about to embark upon. It started after leaving the hospital and hit with full force on the seventh day. Crying was all I seemed to do anymore. It took the littlest things to open the floodgates, and a wave of tears would follow. For about the first three weeks, I cried about three times a day. Judy and Gina both said this was very normal and to just let it happen. I experienced the "baby blues": a mild form of depression that affects more than 80 percent of new mothers, with symptoms that include crying, anxiety, sadness, headaches, exhaustion, feeling unworthy, and irritability. Baby blues can be the result of feeling overwhelmed and tired. Other contributors include:

- the many bodily changes the new mother is experiencing;
- a response to postpartum pain or discomfort;
- illness;
- difficulties during pregnancy;
- concerns about dealing with the new baby or surprise about the amount of work involved in caring for the baby;
- unrealistic expectations of childbirth and parenting;
- a letdown from an exciting event;
- an unexpected pregnancy;
- changes in the family's finances;
- insufficient social or emotional support.[3]

Baby blues usually last from a few days to several weeks. Mine lasted three weeks. Dave was understanding and supportive during these episodes, but I'm sure he secretly watched, ready to diagnose me with postpartum depression (PPD). PPD is a physical illness that affects the brain. It affects between 10 and 20 percent of all women who have given birth, but it is more common among second-time moms than first-time moms. Symptoms include:

- feeling a sense of sadness that doesn't go away;
- frequent mood swings;
- anxiety or guilt.

PPD usually begins two weeks to three months after a baby is born. If PPD is diagnosed, medication is used to

[3]See page 220 for Bibliography.
[4]See page 220 for Bibliography.

treat the illness.[4] My mom had PPD with Deb, and she worried that one of us may have it. Mom ended up calling her doctor, who gave her a prescription. The medicine helped immensely. Mom told Dave to watch for the signs and call our doctor immediately if he thought I had PPD.

At times I wondered if I had PPD, because I began to worry obsessively about Colin. Sometimes my mind would run wild with fears about SIDS, which led me to check on him constantly. Even though I had the monitor on, I could not stop worrying. "What ifs" played tricks on my mind. What if his nose got stuffed up? Would he know how to breathe through his mouth? What if he stopped breathing? What if the blanket fell off and he was freezing to death? What if the blanket fell over his face?

Thoughts like these drove me crazy, prompting me to check on him constantly. Leaning over his crib, I'd strain my ears to catch the rhythmic sounds of his breathing, or I'd watch the rise and fall of his chest. During the night, it was particularly difficult, because I would sneak into his nursery guided only by the night-light in the hallway, which was a godsend gift from Gina.

One night I leaned over the crib to listen to his breathing, I couldn't hear anything. I strained my ears even harder, like a submarine navigator listening to the ocean sounds, for the familiar signs I was trained for. Just one little sigh, one exhale, a slight movement...anything!

I could feel my face getting red with panic as I thought the worst. Please God, don't let it be me. Oh Colin, please do something to let me know you are OK. I moved my hand in front of his nose, waiting to feel a puff of warm air. I just couldn't tell. Ever so gently, I reached over and wrapped my fingers around his tiny little hand. My stomach dropped and tears sprang to my eyes. His hand was cold. Convinced the worst had happened, I grabbed his chest out of fear, and suddenly two arms and legs shot straight out like he was in a free fall. His eyes fluttered wide open and he let out the loudest scream I'd ever heard.

"Oh rats! You dumb ass!" I cussed myself out. He was sound asleep, and I let my crazy mind get the best of me and woke him up. Picking him up, I started walking around his room while trying to calm him down. I was really mad at myself for letting my thoughts run wild, resulting in me waking him up after I'd worked so hard to get him to sleep. I should have known better than to touch his hand, because his hands and feet, if not covered, were typically cold. The silly thing is that each time I checked on him, he was always asleep and happy as a clam. However, I was always convinced there was something wrong. For some reason, I could not accept the fact that I had been blessed with a wonderful, happy, healthy baby. I guess I thought it was too good to be true.

The turning point came when I was telling my mom there was something wrong with Colin's nostril. "Look Mom," I pointed out, "I think Colin has two nostrils in one nostril hole. It must not have developed properly. Should I call the doctor? I don't know what to do."

She took one look up Colin's nose and said, "It's a booger."

"No, it couldn't be that. I'm sure it is something worse." Upon closer inspection, I found to my surprise that, yes, my son had his first booger.

Mom told me I had better work harder to try and relax and just take the "no big deal" approach. She said I was going to develop really bad nerves or drive myself crazy if I didn't relax and enjoy. So, each day I had to force myself to say "no big deal" as I dealt with one thing after another.

Looking back, I think part of this nervousness was from

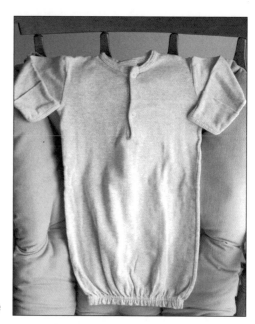

24.1 Layette

my out-of-control hormones, but I also think it was from my lack of confidence about caring for a baby. However, as each day went on, I felt more comfortable handling Colin, changing his diapers, and putting on his clothes. The first three weeks, he wore nothing but the layette outfits with the elastic at the bottom because they were so easy to use. A layette looks like a long dress with an elastic gathering at the bottom, or sometimes it's closed at the bottom with a zipper up the front. (See picture above.)

They were a gift from Gina, but they may as well have been a gift from God. I had never seen a layette before then, but when we started using them, they really were better than sliced bread. Dave and I both loved these outfits, because it was so simple to push the outfit up around Colin's waist or simply unzip it, change his diaper, then pull it back down or zip it back up. It didn't require matching up the snaps or lifting the baby, and it could all be done in a matter of seconds. The layettes proved especially helpful in the middle of the night, when Colin woke up needing changed and fed.

Gina told me to be "stealth-like" during the nighttime feedings. She said to use a minimal amount of light, hence the night-light, and to not talk or make any sounds. The lowest amount of stimulation will keep your baby from fully waking up. So at 3 a.m., I'd enter Colin's room, pick him up, place him on the changing table, slide the layette up around his waist and change his diaper – all while he was screaming his head off. Within a minute, we'd transition over to the rocking chair and begin feeding. At times, Colin didn't even open his eyes, but the room was so dark, there wasn't much to see. After feeding him, the sleeping baby was burrito-wrapped and placed from the waist down on the waterproof pad in his crib.

A great piece of advice I received from my mom was the recommendation to purchase waterproof changing table and crib pads. These covers are the second best things to sliced bread. I can honestly say I used them every day and consider them a must-have. The white pads are 17 inches wide and 27 inches long with the underside consisting of a plastic, vinyl-type material and soft, fuzzy cotton on the top. Basically, these waterproof pads are placed over the terry cloth cover of the changing table pad (cotton side up), protecting the terry cloth cover from getting stained. Several times, Colin peed, and once pooped, all over the changing table before I could get another diaper on him. The waterproof pad simply absorbed the liquid. When the waterproof pad got dirty, I threw it in the washing machine with a load of whites. While it was being washed, I took a spare pad and put it on the changing table. The terry cloth cover and mattress hardly ever got dirty.

For the first four weeks, I also placed the waterproof pads

in the middle of the crib, with the short sides facing the length of the crib. When I put Colin in his bed, I made sure he was on the pad from the waist down. If one of us didn't put the diaper on securely, sure enough the urine would escape and seep all over the crib sheet. The worst thing in the world was wrestling with the crib sheet in the middle of the night because the stink was too strong, the wet spot was too big, or my mind wouldn't relax until the sheet had been changed.

Chapter 25

The Monitor

As each day came and went, Dave and I found our confidence increasing more and more. Compliments not criticism was my constant reminder to praise instead of pick. I found that Dave responded better when I told him what a good job he did. Even if he was doing something different than I would, I bit my tongue and said "good job." If it really irritated me, I would force myself to just walk away, and remind myself that there were several ways of doing things, and my way was not the only way. This thought was reinforced when Dave announced that we had to turn off the baby monitor. I looked at him like he was crazy, because I viewed the monitor as one of our must-have items. Every morning, we transferred the monitor from our bedroom to the kitchen and then back up to the bedroom at night. I found myself constantly looking at that little white box, waiting for the red lights to start dancing. All I needed was one little red flashing light from the monitor, and I had reason to spring into action. It was almost like Pavlov's dog. The red lights would flash, and I responded by becoming Florence Griffith-Joyner, sprinting to get the baby.

Dave told me the monitor was driving him crazy. Being such a light sleeper, he heard every sound Colin made. Whether he was moving his arms or letting out a sigh, Dave heard it. Every sound left him lying in bed, wide-awake, holding his breath while waiting for the familiar wailing. This didn't seem to affect me as much, because I was exhausted at night. At times, Dave woke me up to let me know Colin was crying. Since I was nursing, it was always me that got up, but I used Dave as my alarm clock. Because of this, he was not getting the sleep he needed, resulting in both of us being exhausted and short on patience. During the day, we both dragged ourselves around the house, only doing enough to get by.

In all honesty, the monitor was making me nervous, too. But I thought we had to use one, since everyone else did. Would we be bad parents if we turned off the monitor? What if we couldn't hear him crying? The truth is, turning off the monitor at night turned out to be the best thing we did. At first, I was really unsure about doing it because I worried that I would not be able to hear the baby. I would lie in bed and strain my ears to hear a sound that was not there. After a few nights, I started to relax, because when Colin would cry, there was no mistaking that sound. With a powerful set of lungs and an empty belly, he had no problem letting me know he needed something. He was just 15 feet away in the next room, so his crying would reverberate through the walls and land on my waiting ears.

Chapter 26

Lack of Sleep

As silly as it may seem, the thing I worried about the most while pregnant was the low amount of sleep I knew I'd have to deal with once the baby came. Knowing what it felt like to stay up all night working on school papers and then dragging myself to work and school the next day, I was really dreading this. My friend Judy told me that I'd find myself operating in a fog sometimes, so tired from the lack of sleep, but with enough energy to get the job done.

Here I was in the thick of it, getting up three times at night to nurse Colin. I'd navigate to Colin's nursery by the light of the night-light and enter his room only to be smacked in the face with his screaming fits of hunger. Each cry knocked my senses back to reality and woke up my sleeping brain. I would take him out of the crib and place him on the changing table. I always changed his diaper first, because after he was finished eating, he was most likely sound asleep. I never wanted to wake him after that. After changing his diaper, we would head over to the rocking chair I grew to love. I sat in the chair while feeding Colin and struggled to stay awake. After about two weeks of nighttime feedings, I found my body getting used to sleeping three hours at a clip. I was amazed I could even function like this. But on the flip side, when I decided it was time to sleep, I slept very hard. At times, Dave had to wake me because I didn't hear Colin crying. Other times, Dave would ask if I had heard the torrential downpour or a barking dog. I said no with a smile, because in a way, it was nice to know that I had slept through something he hadn't.

Chapter 27

To Binky or Not to Binky;
That Is the Question

As funny as it may seem, another thing I worried about during my pregnancy was the use of a pacifier. Binky® and Nuk® are two popular brand names. I worried about which to use. Do I want the baby dependent on a pacifier or thumb? I had my pros and cons for both, so I wasn't sure what to do.

Thumb	Pacifier
Pros	**Pros**
• Costs nothing • Within arm's reach	• Can throw away when breaking habit • Frees both hands
Cons	**Cons**
• Could affect front teeth • May be harder to break habit	• Have to buy • May develop habit of getting up at night to put back in mouth. • Keeping track of pacifier.

A few days after we got home, Colin became fussy one evening. Changing his diaper and feeding him didn't help. We were not sure what else to do. After listening to him cry for 15 minutes, I was desperate. Remembering the two new packs of pacifiers Judy gave us, I hurried upstairs and frantically dug through the bag of baby items. Finding them was like discovering gold nuggets. Snatching them up, I ran downstairs, excitedly holding them up in the air as if they were the future to our success.

To Binky or Not to Binky; That Is the Question

I learned that pacifiers are designed for various age groups, with different shaped nipples and colors. There are newborn to 3 months; 3 months to six months, and so on. One package said 0-3 months so I broke it open. Please God, let this work, I pleaded to myself. In went the pacifier, and it worked like a charm. We were so relieved for a moment of peace and quiet. I decided that if Colin found comfort by a pacifier, then we would use it. My sister Deb told me Colin would figure out how to find his thumb in about four weeks. She was right, because around that time, Colin's thumb would occasionally hit the target and he would start sucking. We decided to let him pick what he wanted to use. Surprising to me, I preferred the thumb. My reasoning: I would rather he used his thumb, so I didn't have to get up in the middle of the night to put the pacifier back in his mouth. But we used the pacifier when we needed him to be quiet in public.

Bottom line: We used whatever worked for the situation. We came to realize that we didn't have to commit to one or the other. We used both.

Chapter 28

Colin's Two-Week Checkup

Colin was getting close to his two-week checkup, so I made an appointment. When the day arrived, I was excited to get out of the house, but I was discouraged with how much work it was to get out the front door. I gave myself two hours to get ready, get Colin dressed, pack the diaper bag, grab something to eat, feed him, load the car, and drive to Dr. Morris's office.

Once I got there, I turned into a pack mule. In one arm was Colin in the carrier and from my other shoulder hung his jam-packed diaper bag and my purse. As I waddled to the office door, I realized that I needed another arm. I awkwardly grabbed the door and maneuvered myself through, while my arm ached from the weight of the carrier. With my left arm throbbing from the carrier and my right shoulder weighted down with my bags, I waddled over to the check-in desk. The nurses were so excited to see Colin, and I was just beaming with pride. They ooh'd and ahh'd over him, which of course made me grin from ear to ear. Once we got into the exam room, I was anxious to see what he weighed. At birth, Colin was 8 pounds, 13.5 ounces, and when we left the hospital, he had dropped to 8 pounds, 5 ounces. The nurses said it was very normal for babies to lose weight in the hospital after birth. When Dr. Morris's nurse placed Colin on the baby scale, it read 8 pounds, 6 ounces. I was slightly disappointed, because I viewed Colin's growth as an indicator of the job I was doing. With him only gaining one ounce, I began to worry that my breast milk was not fortified with the essential nutrients he needed. I was relieved when Dr. Morris reassured me that everything was fine. She said his body weight had leveled out and he should start to increase in weight from then on.

Dr. Morris proceeded to examine Colin's circumcision. She removed the small bandage from his penis. She commented on how nicely it had healed and said we didn't have to use the Vaseline and gauze anymore. What a relief. It was one thing less to deal with.

Dr. Morris then checked on his belly button cord. It looked like a brown, shriveled, wrinkled piece of bark, one inch long and crusty from the lack of moisture. It was creepy-looking, because it represented a physical attachment to me, a concept still hard to believe. Dr. Morris said it was drying up nicely and should fall off in the next few days. She told me to continue folding down the top one-inch flap on the waistband of the diaper, so it would not tug or rub against the belly button cord. I also assumed I should continue using the side snap T-shirts until his belly button fell off, because the onesies that snap at the crotch also would rub against the cord.

Dr. Morris went on to check Colin's ears, mouth, and back. She pointed out several pimples with white heads on the bridge of his nose and forehead. "This is basically called baby acne. Don't be surprised if he gets more of these pimples," she warned. "It is very normal for this to happen as Colin's body tries to balance out the natural chemicals within the skin." (I will talk more about baby acne in a later chapter.)

Before I knew it, his exam was over. She looked at me and said, "He looks great! You're doing a good job. Keep up the good work." I beamed with pride and relief. I so intensely wanted to be a good mom. Her praise meant I was heading in the right direction, but I would soon learn there was no such thing as "the perfect mom."

I firmly believe that raising a baby is all about choices. It's about evaluating various situations and facts, then making the best choice for your baby. We soon learned that some of the decisions we made were not the best ones, but it was our choice. If something didn't work, we would simply change our game plan and try something else. It wasn't that we were making bad decisions; it was simply that what we chose didn't work for Colin. It was always a guessing game for us, until something worked.

What I did learn was that things will go right and things will go wrong, but through it all, we would survive. Various situations would make me stronger, strengthening the bond and love between Colin and me, and creating what I now view as "a great mom."

Chapter 29

A Time to Remember

Two days after Colin's checkup, his belly button cord dried up and fell off. After changing his diaper, I looked on the floor and noticed a shriveled, wrinkly piece of something. I hardly recognized it when I picked it up, but to my surprise, it was his belly button cord. While changing his diaper, I hadn't even noticed it was no longer there. For some strange reason that I still can't explain, I decided to save it. Yes, as gross as that sounds, I put it in his "keepsake" box. This box is a future time capsule. It holds all the things I want to show him in the future when we talk about when he was a baby. Several months back, I purchased a box that opens like a book. On the inside of the lid, there are tiny drawers and pockets with the opposite side providing additional storage. The little drawers held both Dave and my hospital bands as well as Colin's ID bracelet. Another drawer contained a new, shiny year 2000 penny, a newly created one-dollar coin, and his hospital cap. In the bottom of the box was a *Columbus Dispatch* newspaper printed on the day he was born; a clipping from the birth section of the newspaper listing our names with "boy" recorded after it; a copy of our hospital bill; a birth record; his first picture, and a journal with comments about my pregnancy. I continued to add to the box, items such as his baptism certificate and a letter from our pastor.

Some day, I will pull this box off the shelf and show him all the things that signify a time of my life when everything came together and I felt like I knew why I was placed on this earth. To me, there was nothing more rewarding than being given the privilege to have and raise a child.

Chapter 30

Bath Time

After giving the base of Colin's naval a few additional days to dry up, it marked the invocation of another big event: Colin's first bath. Dr. Morris told us to wait to give him a bath until his belly button cord fell off. He had not had a bath for three weeks, and I worried this would cause some kind of problem. Of course, Dr. Morris told me infants don't get dirty like kids or adults do. They are simply not active enough. She assured me that if I kept his private parts clean, he could literally go months without having a bath. So here I was, anxious to give him a bath, but too afraid to start the process. That's when Deb came to the rescue.

Deb showed me how to give Colin a bath. We went upstairs to the bathroom, where the counter provided enough room for the plastic baby bathtub. (Several of my friends use their kitchen counter because it provides more counter space.) First, she told me the whole process should last about fifteen minutes but can be stretched out to 30 if you're trying to waste time. Deb said it was good to give the baby a bath before bed because the warm water will relax him and make him tired. Next, she instructed me to get a diaper, some wipes, a T-shirt or onesie, a sleeper, a hooded bath towel, a washcloth, and a large cup. While I retrieved these items, Deb placed Colin on the floor in the middle of our plush bath rug. He lay there all bundled up in a blanket, not knowing what he was in for. Dave came in with the video camera and started recording.

When I returned, Deb had plugged in her space heater and was warming up the room. What a great idea. Since it was the beginning of October in Ohio, the evenings were quite chilly and a baby with wet exposed body parts can get cold very easily. Deb suggested I get a space heater and turn it on 10 minutes before bath time, to warm up the room. She said it takes the chill out of the air when the baby is in the tub. I made a mental reminder to get one at the store. She warned me to place the space heater far away from the bath water.

REMEMBER: A space heater is an electrical device and can cause electric shock if submerged in water. Be paranoid when using this device. Keep it as far away from the baby and water as possible.

Using an extension cord, we placed the heater on the floor next to the bathtub. (One of my friends put it on the counter in the kitchen to let the hot air blow directly on the tub, preventing the baby from getting cold.) Again, make sure it is not close to any water.

Deb then put the tub on the counter (make sure the plug in the bottom of the tub is securely closed). She removed the plastic from the sponge baby headrest and laid it on the back of the tub where Colin's back and head would be. This sponge headrest was awesome, because it prevented Colin from slipping around in the tub and gave me the freedom to use both hands when washing him. (Note: Do not wash the sponge headrest in the washing machine, because pieces of the sponge will break off.) Using the large cup, she filled the tub half full with warm water. Dipping her elbow in the water, she was able to test the temperature to determine if it was too hot. While she did all this, I undressed Colin. As Deb gently placed him in the water, she warned me that he would probably cry the first several times. It was a new experience for him and possibly a little scary. True to her word, he started to cry. I worried that the water was too hot, but Deb was right. It was a new situation for him and he was a little overwhelmed with being in the baby bathtub for the first time. To my relief, he only cried two more times and then grew to love bath time.

Just as Deb was getting ready to wash Colin, he showed her what he thought of the bath. A little fountain went off in between his legs and he proceeded to pee. Deb placed the washcloth over his penis to catch the urine and then threw it in the sink. Next to the tub, Deb had opened bottles of body wash and shampoo. She put some body wash on a clean washcloth and washed his belly, legs, arms, and armpits. "Make sure you wash the creases in his legs near his crotch. That's where poop and pee can collect," she advised. After rinsing the washcloth, she proceeded to wipe his face. Eyes glued to the process, I took mental notes of everything she did. To be honest, it didn't look all that hard, but I was too afraid to step up to the plate. I was glad to watch from the sideline.

Next, Deb took the wet washcloth and squeezed it above Colin's hair as the water ran down the back of his head. She put baby shampoo in her hands, worked up a lather, then ran her hands all over his scalp. The grand finale was when we put warm water in the empty squeeze bottle I brought home from the hospital and squirted the sudsy shampoo from Colin's head. It was so easy to hold his head with one hand while the other hand maneuvered the bottle.

After the bath, Deb picked Colin up, placed him in the hooded towel we spread out on the floor, and wrapped him in it. Keeping him bundled, Deb used the hood from the towel to rub his head until his hair was dry. Next, we put on a fresh diaper, applied baby lotion, dressed him in a T-shirt and layette, and wrapped him back up in a blanket. Holding him in my arms, I inhaled the sweet smell of a clean, fresh baby. I decided nothing smelled better than a baby after bath time. His hair carried the familiar sweet baby smell from the same brand of shampoo used when I was a kid. His body felt extra toasty warm from the warm bath water, which made me want to cuddle with him all night.

Before Deb left, I begged her to cut Colin's fingernails. I was too afraid for fear of cutting them too short, causing them to bleed. For the past three weeks I bit his nails, too afraid to operate the tiny nail clipper. But my attempts to keep his nails short were unsuccessful. After two weeks, he scratched his face and it started to bleed. Too fearful of using the clippers, I did the next best thing. Slipping no-scratch mittens on his hands, I was relieved to know my son could no longer nick and scratch his face. It was funny because it looked like he was wearing little winter mittens or boxing gloves. But I was desperate to keep him from scratching his face until Deb could clip his nails. In the meantime, his nails were growing at an incredible rate, something I never expected. Colin's fingernails were so sharp, they reminded me of puppy teeth, which feel like shards of glass. Deb said the best time to cut fingernails is after bath time because the nails are soft and easy to cut. Another good time is after the baby falls asleep, so he isn't wiggling around.

Using the microscopic fingernail clipper, Deb pressed the skin away from the nail and expertly maneuvered the clipper around each fingernail. Adding to the complexity was the fact that each nail was smaller than a kernel of corn. Deb acted like it was no big deal, while I was on pins and needles. Once she was done, I couldn't believe the whole process was over. Giving Colin a bath didn't seem that difficult, and over time, it would end up being one of my favorite things to do. After giving him his third bath on my own, I was more confident with the process and even grew fearless with clipping his nails. My confidence grew with each experience, which was a good thing. If Colin started kindergarten wearing those no-scratch mittens, people would have been concerned.

Chapter 31

Baby Acne

Colin was 19 days old when the baby acne hit. The few whitehead zits on his face, pointed out by Dr. Morris at his two-week visit, seemed to multiply overnight. It started with 15 pimples on his forehead and nose and then quickly grew to well over a hundred. We grew nervous as we watched more and more whiteheads pop up and spread down his forehead, blanketing his eyelids, the bridge of his nose, and his cheeks. They were so close together that some zits united to form one big pimple. When his eyelids started to swell slightly, that's when I decided to call Dr. Morris. It looked so painful and itchy, and I assumed Colin was miserable. After hearing a panicky new mother on the phone, it was probably easier for the doctor's office to have me come in. So here I was heading back to the doctor's office less than a week after the first visit. When we got there, I wanted to hide Colin from everyone's bulging eyes and tight lips after they peered in his carrier to look at the darling baby they expected to see. My beautiful, angelic baby with smooth, soft milky white skin looked like he did a header into a bowl of oatmeal.

When Dr. Morris came in to see him, she immediately said it was a severe case of baby acne and confirmed that everything was OK.

"Could he be allergic to something? Am I not keeping him clean? I'm using that baby laundry detergent everyone said to use. What am I doing wrong?" I whined. Convinced it was my fault, I was surprised when she told me she saw this all the time.

"It's just his skin balancing out, and it's got to run its course. This is just a stronger case of it, but don't worry, he is not itchy or uncomfortable. It actually looks worse than it is." Dr. Morris recommended I purchase a bottle of Cetaphil gentle skin cleanser and Cetaphil moisturizing lotion. "They are expensive," she cautioned, "but they will last you a very long time. Just a little bit will do the job. Both of these products are fragrance free. The cleanser helps to gently remove the natural dirt and oils from Colin's face while the lotion adds back the moisture to keep his skin from getting dry," she explained.

I wrote it down and decided to stop at the drugstore on the way home. (I later found the generic drugstore brand with the same ingredients at almost half the price.)

Before she left the room, Dr. Morris cautioned, "Whatever you do, as tempting as it may be, don't squeeze these pimples, because they can scar your baby's face." At that point, my sole mission in life was to make sure that not one of those pimples broke. I grew to guard them like a junkyard dog. Colin tended to rub his eyes and touch his face, so I did not want to take any chances. Even though I tried to keep his nails short, back on went the no-scratch mittens.

For the next three weeks, I gently cleansed Colin's face and applied the lotion every day. However, I found myself frequently questioning whether this would work. It wasn't that I doubted the recommendation from my doctor; it was everyone's feedback. People were so willing to offer advice and suggestions; even total strangers would tell me how to treat Colin's baby acne. Due to my lack of confidence and all the feedback, I started doubting if Dr. Morris's treatment was the best solution. I felt guilty, because we trusted Dr. Morris, and we really liked her approach. But if other people dealt with this situation differently, then what was the correct solution? That's when my mom gave me some good advice.

Talking on the phone to her one evening, I vented my frustrations with everyone's suggestions and strong viewpoints.

She advised, "Understand that when people give advice, they are only trying to help. It doesn't mean you actually have to take their advice, but you may want to listen to what they have to say. If it makes sense to you, then try it. If it doesn't and you like your current approach, then thank them for the advice and move the conversation on. People will always offer advice for all kinds of situations. Always, take advice with a grain of salt."

The truth is, I really liked Dr. Morris's approach, so I kept up with it. I learned, through this and future medical situations, to keep Colin's health between Dave, Dr. Morris, and me. Discussing it with others only made me worry and doubt the treatment and myself. I learned to rely on my motherly instincts and do what I thought was best for Colin. At times I even questioned some of the advice Dr. Morris gave us. But once she answered all my questions, I felt more comfortable. For my own peace of mind, it was important for me to believe in my doctor and trust that she was giving me the best medical advice for my son. I believed she was.

I also learned that a wealth of information could be obtained from family, friends, and other parents regarding their experiences. From diapers, clothes, and food, to schedules, nursing, and toys, I learned a lot. Remembering what my mom said, I learned to determine what advice I could use and what to take with a grain of salt.

Chapter 32

The Inevitable: My Six-Week Checkup

Eventually, the time arrived for my six-week checkup at Dr. Morris's office, and I really didn't want to go. Knowing she would perform an internal exam, I seriously thought about canceling my appointment. I was not sure if the stitches had completely dissolved, and my nervousness and fear of experiencing any pain "down there" was still with me. I had not even worked up the courage to look "down there" for fear of what it would look like. I don't know what I expected to see, but maybe I feared what I didn't expect to see. Knowing the exam would have to occur sooner or later, I decided I might as well get it over with.

Getting ready and loading Colin into the car took less than the two hours I initially planned for. With experience from other outings, I had learned how to be more efficient and organized and to plan ahead. A routine for leaving the house had formed, making it easier and less stressful when venturing out. Once we arrived at Dr. Morris's office, my first hurdle was getting on the scale. Curiosity got the best of me and I wanted to see how much weight I had lost. My belly was the size of a volleyball, so I was still wearing my maternity pants. Putting Colin's carrier on the floor, I proceeded to peel away any items that would contribute to my potential bad mood. Stepping on the scale, I prayed the little lever would creep lower and lower toward my pre-pregnancy weight, while the counterbalance would firmly remain at the top. With a "thunk," the counterbalance hit the bottom and then began to balance out. Sarcastically, I thought "Oh, just great!" I had only lost 13 of the 40 pounds I had gained. Subtract 9 pounds for Colin's weight at birth and I was looking at a measly 4 pounds. In the last 6 weeks, my body had only shed a little over a half a pound a week. I was discouraged. But my mood changed when I reached down to pick up Colin's carrier. Looking at his sweet, sleeping baby face, I immediately thought it was all worth it. I'll deal with the weight later.

As we entered the exam room, I was told to strip from the waist down, get up on the exam table, and cover myself with the paper sheet. As I sat there looking at Colin, I just prayed it would hurry up and be over. The nurse came in, took my blood pressure and then Dr. Morris came in. The nurse held Colin while Dr. Morris began the internal exam. Talking to me helped, but my knees were shaking. Once the exam started, I felt a slight pressure "down there," with a little discomfort, but it was not painful. Before I knew it, the procedure was over and she was telling me everything was healing very nicely. What a relief. It was over and it wasn't that bad. I think my mind worked itself up over something that ended up not being bad at all. However, the next thing Dr. Morris said just about knocked me off the exam table.

"So, have you and Dave talked about means for birth control?" she asked.

The thought of any more activity "down there" so soon was enough to push me into postpartum depression. "Oh, you don't have to worry about that. My method of choice is abstinence," I asserted.

Good thing Dave wasn't there; he would have hit the floor.

Dr. Morris proceeded to tell me that we had the green light for sex, but she cautioned us to use two means of protection, such as a condom and spermicide. "Even though you are nursing, there is always the chance you can get pregnant" she warned. Next, she told me that many moms who breastfeed have a high level of prolactin, which causes less estrogen to be produced. As a result, the low levels of estrogen don't stimulate the vagina to be as moist during intercourse. Dr. Morris advised me to purchase an artificial lubricant, such as KY Jelly, but not Vaseline, to help with the dryness.

As she talked about this, my blood started to boil over at the thought of having sex again. I instantly became angry that Dave would even consider something like that. How could he be so selfish to think I was even ready for sex again after all the pain I had endured "down there." As far as I was concerned, having intercourse would hurt and my crotch deserved a break. Another thought dawned on me: Even if I were ready for sex, when in the world would I have time for it? Still trying to learn and balance out my new responsibilities as a mom, my mind and body were consumed with taking care of a baby, two dogs, grocery shopping, cooking, laundry, and cleaning, all while getting up twice a night to nurse.

Remembering where I was, I calmed down and began chatting with Dr. Morris about other things affecting my life. So much had changed. The bleeding had stopped, the hemorrhoids were gone, and my body had adjusted to the low amounts of sleep. I was even learning to multitask and plan again. Heading toward a new type of normalcy, I even found time to cook a meal and do more household chores. We talked briefly about Colin's eating and sleeping schedule, which had taken shape when he was 4 weeks old. With somewhat of a schedule in place, it was so much easier to plan and take care of him now that he had become more predictable. In addition, the breastfeeding was going well, and I found my confidence increasing with it each day.

Our new family was heading back to a normal routine, and it felt good. Although I still felt like this whole baby thing was a guessing game, we got better at determining what Colin needed. The first six weeks were definitely the most difficult, but we had survived and life was good again. Just when we got comfortable with our routine, our lives would be affected by a new factor that presented itself way too soon. I would have to return to work in two weeks.

Getting In Your Groove

Chapter 33

Our First Time Out Without Colin

Colin was 7 weeks old when the big day arrived. It was our fourth wedding anniversary, so we decided to go out for dinner and celebrate. I was excited over the thought of getting out of the house and going to dinner, but my nerves were on edge over the prospect of leaving Colin with a babysitter for the first time. Mom had offered to watch Colin, and surprisingly enough, I was still nervous. The crazy thing was my mom couldn't have been a better choice. The true veteran, who raised five kids and has been around my three nephews since the day they were born, could have done this with her eyes closed. So why was I still nervous about leaving him? What if he cried the entire time we were gone? What if he didn't want to drink a bottle? What if he got scared in his new, unfamiliar surroundings? Mom didn't know the patterns and routines like we did. I feared Colin would be afraid and confused with his new situation.

Determined to be on time for our reservation, Dave pushed and pulled to get the baby and me out the door. As we drove to my mom's house, I mentally reviewed the checklist: diapers, wipes, one gallon zip locking bags for dirty diapers and clothes, extra sleeper, extra onesie, two blankets, a cap, toys, bottles of breast milk, two types of nipples, a burp cloth, and a pacifier.

Arriving at Mom's, my nervousness was noticeable. Chatting up a storm and trying to arrange everything, I peppered Mom with details regarding feedings, diapers, and anything else I could think of. Stalling our departure, I began showing her every item in Colin's diaper bag. Then Dave interrupted, "Your mom knows what she is doing; let's go."

Embarrassed over the thought of telling my mom such novice details, I mentally agreed that it was time to meet the inevitable. We were going out for the first time without Colin.

As we drove to the restaurant, I went though the mental checklist again, making sure I had not forgotten anything. It was so strange to look in the backseat and not see his carrier. After we were seated at the restaurant, Dave and I agreed we would use the time for ourselves and not talk about Colin. But I didn't realize how difficult a task it would be to switch from "mommy mode" to "wife mode." My conscious and subconscious were constantly filled with baby thoughts. Here I was in unfamiliar territory, a nice restaurant with my husband who wanted to spend time with his wife. I found myself a little lost, because the focus on me, as a person, had been pushed to the back of my mind to make room for another role of greater importance. Sitting there looking at Dave, I could see that his mouth was moving, but all I could hear was blah, blah, salad, blah, blah, beer, blah, blah, steak, while my mind raced with thoughts of Colin.

After the waitress took our order, we found ourselves in an awkward moment. We now had the time and energy for adult conversation, but the strange thing was we didn't know what to say that didn't include mention of Colin. Dave proposed a toast and started reminiscing about our wedding and honeymoon. I knew he was trying to distract me from thoughts of the baby. As the conversation progressed, I fought off continual guilt over not thinking about the baby and worrying if he was OK. I struggled to get out of mommy mode, and I tried to have a good time, since it was a rare occasion to be out of the house, alone with Dave and away from Colin.

Dave asked how my book writing was coming along. My excitement and devotion to this new challenge was invigorating. While we ate dinner, I enthusiastically discussed my ideas and plans about various sections and chapters of the book. After dinner was over, I secretly eyed my watch and mentally urged the dessert cart to show up. Once Dave paid the bill, we headed to the car. We were gone only two hours, but it felt like two days. I was excited about the thought of getting back to Colin. I missed him.

Entering Mom's house, I found Colin on a blanket lying on the family room floor. Mom sat next to him showing him cars, blocks, and any object that would hold his attention. A rush of relief came over me when I saw he was OK. We packed Colin's stuff, thanked Mom, and headed home.

Later that evening, while thinking about our first time out, I came to the following conclusion: Leaving Colin for the first time was a nerve-racking experience. I didn't really enjoy being out for the first time, but I knew that at some point, we would have to do it. It might as well have happened sooner than later, because in one more week, I would be heading back to work. If I thought two hours away from Colin was difficult, how would I handle nine?

What I learned about going out without Colin for the first time:

- The first time away from your baby will probably be the hardest. Most likely, you'll fake having a good time.

- Start off with small amounts of time away from your baby. First try two hours, then three, then four. Build up your time, so you can adjust.

- Leave the babysitter your cellular phone number, pager number, or the telephone number where you will be. Tell yourself that if they don't call, it means everything is fine.

- Understand that your mate may not be as worried about leaving the baby. It doesn't mean he doesn't care. It simply means he is looking forward to spending time alone with you.

- Once you leave the house, try to push thoughts of the baby out of your mind and tell yourself it's OK to take a break from the baby. Try to distract yourself with discussions about work, friends, family, weather, and sports.

- Start learning how to switch between mommy mode and wife mode. Finding a balance with both roles will help you feel more comfortable and confident as both a mom and wife.

- Know that you are not a bad person for leaving your baby for a few hours with a babysitter. Try to avoid feeling guilty about not thinking of your baby or being with him. For the mental health of your family, it is important for you both to have breaks to relax and re-energize. In a way, it helps refresh your mind and spirit by disrupting the monotony and routine of baby life.

- Know that leaving your baby with a babysitter gets easier. After four months, you'll be standing on the porch waiting for the sitter to show up, so you can get the heck out of the house and have some fun!

Chapter 34

Day Care

After a lengthy discussion about day care, Dave and I decided to find a woman who took care of kids in her home. Through a friend, I heard about an organization called Action for Children. It is a non-profit, state monitored, home day-care database listing for Columbus, Ohio. This organization has state guidelines and regulations for women who run day-care centers out of their homes. When I called, they gave me a list of names and phone numbers for home-care providers located near my home and work. At 32 weeks pregnant, I started the process. I wanted to make sure I gave myself enough time to locate someone Dave and I felt comfortable with. My goal was to find day-care coverage before I went on maternity leave, so I wouldn't feel the pressure to find someone under a limited amount of time. I knew I wouldn't have very much time to devote to this once the baby arrived, so I pushed to get it done beforehand.

I called six of the 10 people on my list and soon found out the reality of day care. The demand far exceeds the supply. The first six people I called didn't have any opening for newborns, and I found that most providers wanted children in the 1-3 year age range. It is common for home-care providers to watch up to six children with one or two of them being newborns.

When I first started calling day-care providers, I had no idea what to ask them. What was I looking for? What were my requirements? What was reasonable to ask and what was absurd? I felt completely clueless because I didn't even know what it was like to care for a baby, let alone ask if they did the very things I didn't even know of. I felt like an idiot, because I didn't have any questions other than hours of operation, cost, and how many kids they cared for.

After fumbling my way through several calls that resulted in "no openings," I started getting panicky. But more calls began to provide an insight to this new, unfamiliar world. As a result, I came up with a list of introductory questions to ask in the first call. If I liked what they said and had a good gut feeling, I scheduled a visit and asked more detailed questions. See page 190 for a complete list.

After calling everyone on the list, I finally found a very nice lady who took care of children in her home. She had an opening for a newborn around the time I was scheduled to go back to work. Two follow-up visits that included many questions and calls to her references confirmed that the other parents really liked her and she was highly qualified. Nanny, as the children called her, took care of five children. Four were between the ages of 1-4; one other baby was 14 weeks old and then there would be Colin, who would be 8 weeks. She ran the day care in her living room and dining room, which was overflowing with toys and activities. A visit to her house and meeting her family finalized the process and gave us a good gut feeling that she was the one.

What I learned about finding a day care provider:

- The earlier you start looking, the better. If you have a particular day-care center in mind, call when you are 20 weeks pregnant. Ask to be put on their waiting list. Some popular places have an 18-month waiting list.

- If you're looking for a home-care provider, start calling around the 32nd week of your pregnancy.

  - Many home-care providers will know about an opening only one to two months in advance, but some may know of a child going back to school or moving out of town.

- Check your local listings for state-run organizations that list home-care providers.

- Many home-care providers have a network of friends doing the same thing. If one provider is full, ask if they could recommend another home-care provider who might have an opening. That's how I found Nanny.

- Ask co-workers and friends with children where their kids go. A referral can be a godsend and can provide insight into a particular provider.

- Call home-care providers at night, when they have a few free minutes to talk. Calling during the day may be difficult, because the children are there and require attention.

- If traffic and weather are a concern, you may want to choose a provider or day-care center close to you or your spouse's place of employment. Day-care centers often charge a late fee if you don't pick up the child by closing time. ($1 for each minute past closing time, for example.)

- Many places require a deposit to hold a spot for your child.

- For a complete list of telephone and personal interview questions, refer to page 190.

Chapter 35

Getting Ready to Go Back to Work

Two weeks before going back to work, I started pumping and freezing extra breast milk to build up my supply for day care. I planned to pump twice a day at work, but Colin would be eating three times while at day care, so it would leave me one bottle short every day. Building up a large reserve would help me stay ahead. After pumping 3 ounces, I put Colin's name and the date on a piece of masking tape, stuck it to the sandwich bag and put it in the freezer. Nanny told me to do a few "variety packs," so I froze several 2 ounce and 1 ounce bags. I pumped a total of 15 variety bags: seven 3-ounce, six 2 ounce, and two 1 ounce bags.

One week before returning to work, Gina stopped by. She brought over five days' worth of dinners to store in my freezer. I almost started crying. It was the nicest thing she could have done, and I knew that it would really come in handy. I had no idea what to expect upon returning to work, so I knew that any advice she gave me would be useful. She told me to cook and freeze one week's worth of food for my first week back at work. She said the hardest thing at the end of the day was trying to find time to eat once she got home from work. So here I was in the kitchen, making chicken and rice, chili, and meatloaf. Storing them in freezer bags, I added them to my stash of food from Gina. Gina also gave me more great advice:

- Lay out your clothes and iron them the night before. Your morning will be too busy to stand in the closet wondering what to wear.
- Get your bags ready the night before and place them in a pile. The pile may include:

- breast pump and parts, sandwich bags for milk, and brown lunch bags for storage in the refrigerator or freezer at work;
- Diaper bag if day care needs it;
- Purse;
- Briefcase;
- Laptop computer.
- Pack your lunch and put in the refrigerator. (Leave a reminder note on the pile to grab your lunch and the breast milk)
- Lay out your baby's clothes.
- Fill the day-care supply bag with diapers, onesies, sleeper outfits, and a personal check for payment. Most day-care providers require weekly payments made every Monday morning.
- Put the car seat carrier next to the pile with a snowsuit, jacket, or blanket next to it.

Gina told me that she and her husband tried to work out a schedule where she would drop off the baby at day care and he would pick up. They ran into several problems with him being held up at work, resulting in her being stressed out and scrambling to the babysitter at the last minute. They tried switching the schedule, but there always seemed to be problems.

Gina told me this: Plan and operate as if you will be dropping off and picking up. Go about your routine, and if Dave offers to drop-off or pick-up, consider it a bonus. It was by far the best advice she could have given me, because we quickly experienced the same drop-off and pickup problems, and it was very stressful and frustrating. Once I started operating under Gina's advice, my stress level, frustration, and chaos decreased. Even though this put more of the work on me, it was better than being stressed out and mad at Dave all the time.

Three days before returning to work, Colin and I went to Nanny's to drop off his baby stuff. Nanny said it was easier to bring everything over beforehand, so I wouldn't have to deal with it on the first day. She also said I'd have enough on my mind without being burdened with all of his necessities. That day, we took over his Pack 'N Play portable crib, mattress, fitted sheet, 25 diapers, two onesies, two sleepers, one can of formula (in case something happened and Nanny had to use it), and my entire stash of breast milk. Once we got everything stored in his personal drawer, we were ready for Monday.

What I learned about getting ready to go back to work:

- Start pumping breast milk one month before going back to work. Build up the biggest supply you can. Even though it seems like a lot, you will go through it very quickly, as your milk supply may decrease due to stress and less time to pump.

- Freeze a week's worth of food so the convenience of popping something into the microwave at the end of the day lessens one burden on your new schedule.

- Get organized by placing all your stuff in a pile the night before and laying out your clothes.

- Talk about the drop-off and pickup schedule with your spouse. If you don't think he can commit to this task due to work demands, just plan on doing it all yourself. But if he can take the baby to day care it is a huge help and may mentally lessen your stress and anxiety about leaving your baby.

- Get organized with your day-care provider before you go back to work. If she needs supplies, bring them over a few days before, so you don't have to lug everything in on your first day.

Chapter 36

Going Back to Work

The alarm went off Monday morning and I felt like the race started. The next 24 hours went something like this:

6 a.m.	Alarm went off
6:00 – 6:15	Took shower
6:15 – 6:35	Put on makeup and styled hair
6:35 – 6:40	Got dressed (thank God my clothes were laid out)
6:45 – 6:50	Ate bowl of cereal
6:50 – 6:55	Loaded pile of bags in my car
6:55 – 7:25	Woke Colin, changed his diaper, nursed and burped him
7:25 – 7:30	Put Colin in snowsuit, secured him in carrier, and got him in the car
7:30 – 8:00	Drove to Nanny's and then to work
10:30 – 11:15	Pumped breast milk, stored milk in refrigerator, and cleaned out parts
2:30 – 3:15 p.m.	Pumped breast milk, stored milk in refrigerator and cleaned out parts
4:50 – 5:00	Stopped working, picked up breast milk from refrigerator and left work
5:00 – 5:25	Battled traffic to get to Nanny's on time
5:25 – 5:40	Arrived at Nanny's, bundled Colin up, and got out the door
6:00 p.m.	Arrived at home
6:05	Nursed Colin because my boobs were ready to explode
6:30	Finished feeding him; Dave arrived home
6:35	Changed clothes and popped frozen dinner into the microwave

6:45 – 7:15	Fed the dogs, ate dinner, and did the dishes
7:15 – 8:30	Played with Colin
8:30 – 9:00	Fed Colin, put him to bed, got my pile ready, laid out my clothes
9:30	Went to bed
1 a.m.	Got up to feed Colin
4:30 a.m.	Got up to feed Colin
6 a.m.	Alarm went off

Going back to work was not easy. My first day back, I had mixed emotions. I was excited to get out of the house, see everyone, and get back to the job I loved. But I missed Colin terribly. He had been with me for the last 11 months. Granted, nine of those months were in my belly, but he had always been with me. Suddenly I was away from him for large periods of time. Expecting me to experience separation anxiety, Nanny told me to call any time to check on how he was doing. However, after one call and hearing him crying in the background, it just about broke my heart. I decided it was better for me not to call unless it was necessary.

My first week back at work was chaotic and stressful, because I didn't have a routine established while trying to keep up with all my new responsibilities. Watching the clock and trying to keep one step ahead left me exhausted at the end of the day. As I drove like a madwoman to pick up Colin on time, my energy and excitement increased over the thought of getting back to my baby. When I picked up Colin, he looked exhausted, with tired lines under his droopy eyes. Going from a quiet house to an active environment left him overstimulated, but after a few days, he started to adjust. Sometimes Colin fell asleep on the way home from day care, and I never knew if I should wake him to relieve my aching breasts or let him sleep so I could eat. I started letting him sleep for 45 minutes, so I could change my clothes, take care of the dogs, and make dinner. On other evenings, when he was wide-awake when we got home, I would feed and play with him until around 7 p.m., when he would doze off. I would make dinner while he took a 30-minute power nap. I'd wake him up at 7:30 and then keep him up until 8:30 or 9. Then I would change his diaper, feed him, and put him to bed. Usually he was exhausted by then.

As each week went by, I began to settle into my routine and anticipate what needed to be done. I even learned how to finagle the system to make it work for me. Little things like washing my hair every other day or wearing clothes that didn't need ironed allowed me to hit the snooze button. Packing my car the night before or eating Pop-Tarts in the car gave me more time in the morning with Colin. Learning these little tricks provided flexibility, and I took what I could get. I was determined to make all of this work. If millions of women could balance a career and a family, so could I!

What I learned as a first time mom returning to work:

- Plan a schedule of what you need to do to get out of the house, and stick to it.

- Expect to cry the first day. It is stressful, overwhelming, and emotionally heart-tugging when you leave your baby at day care for the first time.

- Know that your situation will get better once you settle into your new routine. Not knowing what you should be doing next is difficult, but it does get better.

- Stay organized and plan one step ahead. This will cut down on you feeling overwhelmed and stressed.

- Write down the feeding and napping schedule your baby develops at day care, so you know what to expect on the weekends.

- Always keep a bag containing diapers, a onesie, and a sleeper in your car. Should you forget your weekly supply, you've got enough to hold you over until you can bring the week's supply the next day.

- If you're breastfeeding, don't be surprised if your milk supply goes down. Stress and decreased nursing sessions have that effect. Also, if you get sick, your milk supply can go down. Nursing your baby in the evening will help keep your supply up.

- Before returning to work, determine where you can express milk at work and how you will store it. Remember: If there is a community refrigerator, put your name on the bag with a note: "Do not toss. Breast milk." A janitor, while cleaning the freezer, threw out three days' worth of my breast milk. I was devastated!

- Take advantage of conveniences, such as getting a cleaning lady, if you can afford it, so you can spend time with your family on the weekends.

- Try to balance out the workload. Working full time, caring for a baby, doing laundry, cooking, cleaning, and managing everyday responsibilities takes a lot of energy. There just aren't enough hours in the day to get it all done. Instead of getting burned out or resentful, work to balance the responsibilities or accept the fact that some things will have to give. Your time is now precious, so you may want to spend it on the things that count!

Chapter 37

Sex For the First Time

After we got the green light for sex, I dreaded the big event. Convinced it was going to hurt "down there," I was fearful of having intercourse. After my six-week appointment, I avoided all sexual advances from Dave for the next four weeks. At that point in my life, I couldn't have been less horny. I'm not sure if it was because I was breastfeeding or because my hormones were still out of whack, but I didn't feel sexual or have any drive to make love. Plus, after working all day and taking care of Colin at night, I would rather sleep during any free time.

One night, after I put Colin to bed, the big event arrived. We headed upstairs, but I was dragging my feet the whole way. It was not fair for me to put it off, so I decided I might as well force myself to be pleasant and get it over with. I was tired, hungry, stressed, and nervous. Add to that the potential pain from intercourse and I was on the verge of being a raving bitch. When I got into the bedroom, I removed the KY Jelly tube from the drawer of my nightstand. Remembering what Dr. Morris said about possible problems with dryness from nursing, I had it ready. But I wasn't sure how to use it. To be honest, I wasn't sure if it goes on the outside or inside of me, so I looked for the instructions, which said: "Use as needed." "Oh great," I thought. "This helps me – not at all!" (I found out it goes on the outside.)

Looking over at Dave, who was acting like a kid on Christmas morning, I asked him to get the condoms. I could see the excitement drain from his face.

"I can't believe I'm married and I have to use a condom," he moaned. "Please don't make me use them," he begged.

"If you get me pregnant tonight, we'll never have sex again," I said. The thought of "chancing it" scared the shit out of me. The thought of going through all the pregnancy stuff again, with a 10-week old baby, while working full time, made my stomach hurt. There was no way I was going to chance it.

Searching high and low for the condoms, Dave became frantic at the thought of losing out on his opportunity. "Try your tool box," I suggested. I remembered seeing a strand of them in the bottom of the metal box while looking for a nail. I thought it strange at the time, but hey, if he considered them a tool, well then, whatever. Before he went downstairs to check, he pulled a piece of lingerie out of my dresser drawer and asked me to put it on. Wanting to be a good sport, I grudgingly agreed. Self-conscious about my body and the extra weight, I was nervous about Dave seeing my larger butt, hips, thighs and "beer belly" stomach, not to mention the stretch marks.

While he ran downstairs, I stripped and slipped the "little number" over my head. To my horror, it stopped above my chest. I thought a little "tug" would allow it to slink down the rest of my body, but it moved an inch and held its ground at the top of my chest. With arms pinned in the "reach for the sky" position, I could feel my face getting red with embarrassment. "Oh my God, I'm stuck." Attempts to reach down and pull it back over my head were futile. All of the sudden, I could hear Dave charging back up the stairs. Not knowing what else to do, I panicked and ran into the bathroom. "Oh, this will help my situation," I sarcastically thought. Standing in the bathroom with arms in the air, nude from the chest down, my mind raced for a solution. Just then, the door swung open and Dave stood there like a deer frozen in the headlights. The corners of his mouth edged upward, and we both burst out laughing. Falling to the floor, he laughed until his sides hurt.

Meanwhile, I stood there red-faced, laughing so hard the tears streamed down my face, all while my arms were still waving above me. Dave stood up and helped me get the contraption off. "Are you still in the mood?" I joked.

"Yeah, but the expiration date on the condoms was four years ago so we should probably pass on this tonight," he said. "I'll get more this week."

What I learned after we finally had sex for the first time:

- There is no good time for making love. Your new, busy life will try to consume your every waking moment, leaving no time for intimacy. Making time is very important to bring your relationship back to a certain level of intimacy.

- Be realistic. Don't expect the first time to be romantic, spontaneous, and enjoyable.

- Make sure to use some means of protection unless you are OK with your children being close in age. You can get pregnant quickly after having your first child. (You may want to discuss various means of birth control with your doctor to determine the best solution for you and your spouse.)

- If you're nursing, you may want to purchase an artificial lubricant, just in case you experience dryness.

- Intercourse may be uncomfortable the first time especially if you've had an episiotomy. You may want to be on top, so you can control penetration.

- If you are breastfeeding, wear a sexy bra or something to cover your breasts. They may leak without you knowing it.

- If you are nervous about making love for the first time since the birth of your baby, talk to your spouse about it. Express your concerns, so he understands why you may be hesitant and how important it is to take things slowly.

- Sex does get better! Just give it time as your new roles balance out, giving you the confidence to switch into wife mode and enjoy.

Chapter 38

How The Dogs Adjusted

Being "dog people," Dave and I were concerned about how our dogs would react and adjust to the new baby. For the past five years, Kassie and Willie were our babies and received all the attention. Now they faced strong competition. With help from our dog trainer, we began the transition from a family of four to a family of five.

During the first three days with Colin, both dogs were wired with unbridled energy as they followed us around the house, constantly wanting to see the baby. As Colin consumed our time, we noticed an immediate change in their behavior. Kassie, our female dog, who favors Dave, was continually trying to vie for his attention when he held the baby. While Dave sat in his recliner, Kassie would stick her nose in the baby's face. At first, Dave became irritated with her intrusions and he pushed her face away, telling her "No." After Dave switched the baby to the other arm, we realized she was competing for his attention. Noticing this, we tried something different. When Kassie came over and stuck her nose close to the baby, Dave petted her a few times and told her "good girl." She would smile and eventually walk away. Other times, Dave would call Kassie to him to pet and praise her. Kassie wanted to know she was still "daddy's girl" and after a few days of doing this, she stopped being so needy. At times, her behavior wore on Dave's nerves, but he wanted to give her positive reinforcement around Colin so she would not feel threatened.

Willie, our male dog, who favors me, handled the situation differently. Turning his back to me, he would lie on the floor and pout. Mad at us for not giving him the time and attention we lavished on him before, he sulked. Determined to make this a good transition, even though I was exhausted, I took the extra time to talk to him and baby him, especially while holding Colin. Willie wanted to know that he was still my baby and that I would continue to lavish attention on him. Even though more of my focus and attention was spent on Colin, I had to make a conscious effort to acknowledge and praise Willie.

As our time was stretched thin, we continually struggled with giving the dogs enough attention. Reminding us of this, Willie began acting up by grabbing pacifiers and walking around the house with them in his mouth. At first, it was funny seeing our big, furry tough guy walking around with a pink plug in his mouth with the pacifier handle swinging up and down. We laughed and teased him, so he learned that grabbing a pacifier would get him attention. Our mistake was reinforcing this behavior. After awhile, it grew irritating as we constantly had to fish them out of his mouth. We scolded him when he did this, so he started grabbing Colin's cloth toys, especially the ones with squeakers in them. Willie, who loved his stuffed toys, tried to claim ownership to Colin's toys. To break this habit, we began to make a concerted effort to give him more attention when he was being good. We also kept the pacifiers out of his reach, but when he did grab them, we ignored him. Getting no attention for his behavior was uneventful, so he stopped doing it.

As for the cloth toys, we had a few casualties, but it got better. When Willie grabbed a cloth toy, we removed it from his mouth and said "No" or "bad boy" and then withdrew any attention toward him. Willie knew these commands were not good, and he didn't like being ignored, so he learned which toys were his and which were Colin's. When Colin received a new toy, we showed the dogs. When Willie tried to put it in his mouth, a sharp "No" would let him know it was off-limits. We stopped buying the cloth toys for Willie and started buying more chew sticks to occupy his time. However, cloth toys continued to be a never-ending battle as more and more entered the house. We just needed to be patient and teach Willie which toys were off-limits.

Our next hurdle was to teach the dogs how to interact with visitors. Not wanting the dogs to get protective of strangers holding Colin, we asked our guests to give the dogs treats while they held the baby. We wanted to reinforce with the dogs, through treats and attention, what a good thing this baby was.

Before Colin, our dogs were definitely creatures of habit. Once Colin came home, the lack of a schedule caused us to struggle with keeping up. So consumed with caring for the baby, we forgot at times to feed the dogs or let them out. This disruption in their routine, along with lack of sleep from all the activity, left them irritable and exhausted. Not accustomed to Colin's crying and my being up every three hours in the middle of the night, they were low on energy and patience. Our solution was to get them back on a routine. We made a point to feed and let them out around the same time every day. Dave started taking them for a walk in the evening, so they could stretch their legs and get away from the baby. As a result, they were too tired from their walk to notice my getting up at night. As time went on, they adjusted to all the noise and learned to sleep through anything. With a lot of patience, treats, discipline and structure, Kassie and Willie adjusted to the new addition of our family. Little did they know that the gravy train would soon arrive when Colin started eating people food from his high chair. Life would definitely be good again for the dogs.

What I learned through the assistance of our dog trainer about helping the dogs adjust:

- Before the baby arrives, play a tape of a crying baby, at low volume, to get the dog familiar with the sound.

- Slowly cut down on the amount of attention given to your dog before the baby is born.

- Allow the dog to sniff a T-shirt your baby has worn before you bring home the baby.

- Don't separate the dog from the baby.

- Make a point to give your dog some one-on-one time.

- Reinforce good behavior with treats.

- Don't encourage "cute" behavior, such as grabbing toys.

- Set limits with your dog about what he can and can't do.

- Take the dog for a walk to work off extra energy.

- Watch for signs of pouting or "intrusions" for attention.

- Contact your vet or find a recommended dog trainer for help and support during this transition.

Chapter 39

First Time Sick

I firmly believe the first time your baby is sick is truly the initiation into parenthood. Your senses will be pushed into overdrive, as you continually try to figure out what is wrong and how to make things better. Worrying is all you can do, because it is really the only thing you have any control over. However, know that once you get over this hurdle, you can get through anything. My best advice for this...

Get ready to be pooped on, peed on, barfed on, drooled on, sneezed on, and snotted on.

Having a sick baby is the worst part of being a parent. Let me explain. As I expected, Colin, who was now 4 months old, picked up a flu virus from one of the kids at day care. After waiting for it to happen, it finally arrived. Colin was sick for the first time.

The initiation started with a runny nose, a fever, sneezing, and a cranky attitude. He added diarrhea to the mix, which added a new color to the stool spectrum as neon yellow poop magically appeared in his diaper. It stunk so bad that not even a diaper pail could mask the stench. It was at this time that I learned how to control my gag reflex. Dave and I resorted to the "rock, paper, scissors" method to see who would challenge fate and survive. Next came the dreaded throwing up.

As I sat in the rocking chair feeding Colin a bottle, my mind raced with thoughts of how to make him feel better. What should I do? Take his temperature? Feed him? Am I keeping him hydrated? Does he have a fever? Should I call the doctor? After he finished his bottle, I gently placed my dozing baby in his crib. Suddenly, his eyes fluttered open and formula started pouring from both corners of his mouth. Panic set in. I feared he would choke, so I scooped him back up. Once I did that, it seemed to stop. "Are you OK?" I gently asked, trying to sooth him as I cuddled him against my body. Lifting his head off my shoulder, he looked at me with those beautiful dark blue eyes and promptly threw up all over me. I'm not talking about a little bit of spit dribbling out the side of his mouth; I'm taking about "Exorcist"-type projectile vomit that rushed out of his mouth, ricocheted off my chest, and landed everywhere. I stood there holding my poor sick baby as hot, slimy, stomach acid-smelling vomit ran down my cleavage. I remember thinking, "Welcome to parenthood."

What I learned the first time my baby was sick:

- Expect to get up in the middle of the night to give medicine or sooth the baby back to sleep.

- Spend the money and purchase a digital thermometer. Trying to take the temperature of a squirming kid is easier when the readout is given in three seconds.

- Don't be afraid to call your doctor's office if your baby is sick. Write down the symptoms and take the baby's temperature before you call. (Possible symptoms: runny nose, fever, unusual stool color, coughing, wheezing, rash, whining, continual crying)

- Purchase a medicine dropper and measurement vile with milliliter, teaspoon, and tablespoon measurements on it. Most prescription medicines for your baby do not come with a dropper or means to administer the drug.

- When administering liquid medicine, try placing only the baby bottle nipple in the baby's mouth. Next, using the medicine dropper, slowly squirt the liquid down in the nipple. Since your baby knows how to suck from a nipple, it is easier to administer medicine through the nipple than to drain the medicine down the back of his throat.

Chapter 40

The Weight

For everything women go through to have babies, our bodies should be rewarded for their efforts. Automatically losing all the pregnancy weight, plus an extra ten pounds for being such a good sport, sounded reasonable to me. But that was not the case.

After gaining 40 pounds during my pregnancy, I was determined to shed the weight soon after the baby arrived. The first six weeks, my belly shrank from the size of a beach ball to a volleyball. However, being too darn busy, I hardly had the time to focus on losing the weight. Heck, I was lucky to even find the time to grab something to eat, let along determine if it was healthy or not.

After eight weeks, I suddenly found my body in an in-between state. No longer was I big, round, and pregnant, nor was I lean, slender, and toned. This was a difficult mental state to be in, because I had never been overweight. Granted, I just had a baby, but I always felt good about my body, and now I didn't. I longed to wear my old clothes and feel confident, sexy, and appealing. But I had to wear my maternity pants for the first four months after the baby arrived, because I couldn't button my pants over my "jelly belly." Dave hounded me to go buy some new clothes, but I didn't want to spend the money on larger-size pants and shirts and get comfortable with the larger size. I wanted an incentive to lose the baby weight and get back to my original size. Wearing those maternity pants with the big panel was my huge incentive to get out of them. I half expected to lose the weight right away from my busy lifestyle, but those darn 15 pounds were determined to hang on, like lampreys on a shark. After five months, I had to remind myself to be realistic.

I received some really good advice from, of all people, our taxman, Scott. He said, "It took you 9 months to put on the weight, so give yourself 9 months to take it off." For some reason, that statement always made me feel better, because I felt an incredible amount of pressure to lose the weight right away. It seems like the "new norm" is for moms to shed the baby weight in only a few months. Here I was, five months later, still carrying the extra weight.

At six months, I decided it was time to "get busy." Nine months was my goal to lose all the weight, and it was fast approaching. If I held the secret to losing baby weight, I'd probably be a billionaire, but unfortunately, I don't. While watching what I ate and keeping myself busy, here is what I also did to help shed the unwanted pounds:

What I did to help lose weight:

- I didn't keep any junk food in the house. When you're feeling down, it's easy to grab that half-gallon of ice cream and a big spoon.

- I switched back to three meals a day instead of many mini-meals.

- I started drinking 64 ounces of water each day. It helped to have a 32-ounce bottle with a big plastic straw, so I could chug the water faster. I drank 32 ounces by noon and 32 ounces by 5 p.m.

- I avoided eating anything after 8 p.m.

- I started walking my dogs 2 miles every night, no excuses. I actually found it nice to get out of the house for 45 minutes by myself to enjoy some peace and quiet while Dave watched the baby.

- If I needed to snack during the day, I'd eat a piece of fruit or chug a glass of water. Not quite the candy bar I wanted, but I just had to get through the craving and then I'd be OK. (Avoid the vending machines at work by keeping no change in your wallet.)

- I packed my lunch for work, so I didn't eat fried fast food with their enormous portions... "Yes, I'd like to enormousize that order to the bushel of fries, a keg of Pepsi, and the side of beef burger." Fried food is tempting, but don't do it.

- I started doing stomach crunches to help tone my flabby stomach. Starting out doing five one day, I added five each day thereafter. If I skipped a day, I'd cut five off, but my goal was to keep adding five on each day.

- I built up from one set of 20 squats to three sets of 20, three times a week. If my butt wasn't sore, then I wasn't doing them right.

- A friend told me to contact my local aerobics or workout center. Many locations will give you a free aerobics membership if you babysit in their nursery once or twice a week.

- I had to keep reminding myself: It took nine months to put on the weight, so give yourself nine months to take it off.

Chapter 41

Sleeping Through the Night

When Colin was 3 months old, I was desperate for him to sleep through the night. The lack of sleep and working all day left me exhausted and irritable. After I fed Colin at 8 p.m., he would then wake up at 1 a.m. and 4 a.m. Back in bed at 4:30 a.m., I would then get up at 6 to get ready for work. Craving more than four hours of sleep at a time, my mind searched and raced for a solution. The reoccurring comment I heard from everyone was "Give him rice cereal at night to fill his belly. That will get him to sleep through the night." Even though my doctor said to wait until he was 4 months old, I was desperate and willing to introduce rice cereal early if it meant he would sleep longer. So one night, using advice from my boss, I cut an X in the baby bottle nipple so the rice cereal could pass through. I made a 4-ounce bottle of breast milk and mixed in two tablespoons of rice cereal. After shaking it, I watched the cereal ooze down the sides of the bottle. Convinced this was my salvation, I bargained with Colin while Dave fed him his bedtime bottle. "Oh please, Colin, if you sleep through the night, I'll buy you a pony." For the health of my body and mind, I really needed this to work. But at 1:30 a.m., I heard the familiar call for "room service." As I headed to Colin's nursery, the tears welled up in my eyes as my tired and aching body accepted defeat. We'll try it again tomorrow night, I decided, and I'll mix in a larger amount of rice cereal.

The next six nights, Colin's bedtime bottle evolved into the consistency of a milkshake. Even though we loaded up the bottle with rice cereal, he always woke up hungry around 1:30. Desperate, I called my doctor's office. "Please tell me the secret to get him to sleep through the night," I begged. The nurse suggested I read a popular book on how to get your baby to sleep through the night.

My blood was boiling. Ending the call, I sat at my desk furious. I angrily thought: "I'm up at 6 a.m. and at work by 8. I pick Colin up at 5:30 p.m., feed him, make dinner, take care of the dogs, feed him at bedtime, get ready for the next day, and I'm in bed at 10 p.m. Plus, I'm getting up twice in the middle of the night for feedings. When in the $*$$% does she think I have time to read a book." I was at my wit's end.

Networking with friends, I received numerous suggestions to get Colin to sleep through the night. Over the next month, we tried everything from putting more rice cereal in his bedtime bottle, to letting him cry himself back to sleep. Simple suggestions such as putting the pacifier back in his mouth failed; Colin spit it out before I even got out of the nursery. Rocking him back to sleep only worsened the situation, because he would wake up as I put him back in his crib. I knew babies slept through the night at different ages, but why wasn't anything working? The most difficult part was trying to focus on the entire situation. I was so darn busy and tired, I couldn't see the forest for the trees. Then it dawned on me one night: Call the Pro. Deb will know what to do. Why didn't I think of her sooner?

That weekend, I called Deb and told her how frustrated I was. Colin was 17 weeks old, and our situation seemed to get worse. Exhausted by 8 p.m., Colin would fall asleep, so we put him to bed. Our feedings shifted to midnight, 3 a.m. and 5 a.m. I was a walking zombie.

Deb suggested I do the following:

- Keep Colin up until 10 p.m. every night. Let him take an evening nap, about 30 minutes, so he can stay awake until 10. Either let him sleep on the way home from day care and while you're making dinner, or let him fall asleep around 7 or 7:30 for 30 minutes.

- Build your way up to 10 p.m. Start off by keeping him awake until 8:10 one night, then 8:20 the next night, and so on. He will be cranky and paw at your nerves, but know that for every minute he is awake during the evening, it is a minute he will be sleeping at night.
- When 9:45 rolls around, change his diaper and put him in thick, warm pajamas.
- At 10 p.m., when you feed him a bottle, make sure he is very hungry. Feed him at 6:30 p.m. and then hold him off until his 10 p.m. bottle.
- At 10, Deb said, nurse him from both breasts and then feed him another 2 ounces from a bottle. I ended up pumping 2 ounces in the early evening and putting it in the refrigerator. Deb said the objective was to get Colin to drink as much as possible. Load him up with a full belly. Then, exhausted from being up so late, he would be too tired to wake up in the middle of the night.
- Don't let Colin fall asleep while feeding him, she warned. Try to keep him awake by rubbing his head and back. Other tricks include rubbing the underside of his chin and talking to him.

With this advice, we put the plan into action. We started keeping Colin up 15 minutes longer than the night before until we reached 10 p.m. Most times, he was cranky and miserable, but I was determined to get him to sleep through the night. At times, Dave wanted to cave in and put Colin to bed early, but I'd turn into a raving bitch. He wasn't the one who was exhausted from getting up with the baby in the middle of the night. I just knew in my heart that if Colin would start sleeping through the night, I'd be a whole new person. I had to stick to the plan for sanity's sake.

As Colin started to go to bed later, the midnight feeding disappeared. Feeling hope and encouragement, we pushed to keep him up later. One night, we made it to 9:30 and then Dave fed him. It had become a ritual for Dave to give him his bedtime bottle. We put him to bed at 9:50, and I was hopeful. That night, I went straight to bed after putting him in his crib.

I awoke to the aching of my breasts. Squinting at the neon green, digital readout on the clock, my eyes bugged out of their sockets. Expecting the clock to say 3 a.m., it read 4:22. "Oh my gosh! He's sleeping, he's doing it," I excitedly thought. My mind raced as it calculated the amount of sleep I had received. Six hours and 22 minutes of solid, sound sleep. I was ecstatic, but not for long. My breasts, expecting to feed two times at night, were ready to explode. Should I go in and feed him or let him sleep? Not wanting to ruin a good thing, I went downstairs and pumped a bottle. At 5 a.m., I heard him start to cry, but I didn't even mind. I had six hours and 22 minutes of uninterrupted sleep. I could deal with that.

A week later, on a Saturday morning, I rolled over in bed and realized the edges of our window shades streamed with early daylight. Looking at the clock, it read 7:02 a.m. "Holy shit! Colin just slept through the night!" So excited, I woke up Dave to tell him my great news. Letting out a groan of acknowledgement, he rolled back over. I realized that I had slept eight hours straight, and I felt like I could run a marathon. Life was definitely getting better.

Once Colin started sleeping through the night, we slowly began to decrease his bedtime. Starting at 10 p.m., we backed down 10 or 15 minutes every few days. Not wanting to jinx myself, we took it slow. Eventually, we settled on a bedtime of 8:30. Colin started sleeping from 8:30 p.m. to 7 a.m.

Once I started getting eight hours of continuous sleep, I felt like a whole new person. I was happy and cheerful and my brain could function, think, and plan again. The old me was back, and it felt good.

What I learned about getting Colin to sleep through the night:

- Every baby is different, and sleeping through the night may not occur for several months down the road. A few moms have been lucky at eight weeks, but plan on getting up at least once in the middle of the night for the next three to five months.

- One of the many ways to get your baby to sleep through the night is to keep him up until 10 p.m., feed him a big bedtime bottle, then put him to bed. (See bullet points above for more details.)

- Once he starts sleeping through the night, slowly back down his bedtime to a reasonable time that works for everyone.

- You may find your baby sporadically waking up in the middle of the night, but eventually those episodes start occurring fewer and farther between.

- If you want to introduce rice cereal, but don't want to use a spoon just yet, cut a small X in a baby bottle nipple, so the rice cereal can pass through. Add the rice cereal to the formula or breast milk. You may want to start out with one teaspoon for every 2 ounces and then gradually increase it. Note: Rice cereal contains iron and can cause constipation.

- Once your body adjusts to getting eight continuous hours of sleep, you'll feel like you can conquer the world, ready to deal with anything. Life truly gets better after this!

Chapter 42

Staying Home

Back at work for six weeks, I finally felt like I was in a routine. I had my mornings down to a science, as I expertly maneuvered getting to work on time. Doing more by 8 a.m. than I ever thought humanly possible, I was determined to make it work. As each day went by, I felt more stressed and frustrated with the fact that my days were a blur and ended so quickly. My time with Colin was precious, as I refused to allow anything else to get in the way, including my writing. My overwhelming desire to write a book about what I learned and experienced consumed my mind at work. The job I loved and thrived at now held very little interest. I was at a crossroads.

One weekend, while Colin was taking a nap, I sat down and wrote out all of our expenses. After cutting out most of our "extras," I realized we could probably live on one salary. It would definitely be a huge adjustment to our lifestyle, but staying home with Colin and writing my book was what I really wanted to do. However, I was terrified of pulling the trigger.

Having been so focused on my career and education, I automatically assumed it would be no big deal to go back to work and resume the life I was accustomed to. Working for the past 14 years, I couldn't imagine what it would be like to give all that up and stay home. What would I do with myself all day? How bored would I get? Would I feel challenged and fulfilled? Would my mind be stimulated? My biggest fear was losing myself among dirty diapers, cooking, cleaning, laundry, and motherhood. I knew that when our baby was born, I would love my baby, but I never imagined the pull to be a stay-at-home mom would be so strong that I'd want to give up the very thing I had worked so hard to achieve.

Dave and I were also comfortable with our lifestyle. We loved to travel, shop, socialize, participate in activities, and basically spend money. Being the anal one with our money, I always kept it in check, but I was always able to produce funds to cover whatever we wanted to do. If I quit my job and stayed home, our budget would be so tight we couldn't afford to do the things we loved. In addition, we would definitely have to follow our new budget, as my abilities to produce funds in the past would not be the case anymore. Could we do this? Could we make it work? I guess what I was really asking myself was could "I" do this? Could "I" make it work?

Revisiting our budget, I wanted to make sure I included all expenses. Here's what I did to come up with a budget:

- I made a list of every monthly expense, no matter how small the amount. Be honest. The list included:
    - mortgage or rent
    - car payments
    - insurance (home, auto, etc.)
    - utilities (gas, electric, phone, cable, water & sewer)
    - credit cards
    - student loans
    - investments
    - gasoline
    - groceries
    - cellular phones, pagers, Internet accounts
    - prescriptions and doctor visits
    - activities (i.e. golf, baseball and football games)
    - spending money allowances

- eating out at restaurants
- diapers, wipes, formula (about $150/month)
- clothes and toys for the baby ($75)
- clothing and household expenditures
- any other expense throughout the year, such as:
  - license plate renewals
  - oil changes
  - vet bills
  - birthdays
  - Christmas
  - vacations
- Add up all the expenses for the month, leaving out any other expenses throughout the year.
- Next, total your estimated "throughout the year" expenses and divide by 12. Add that amount to your monthly expense column.
- Figure your family's monthly net income.

Our monthly expenses exceeded Dave's monthly net income, so I started cutting the "extras" until our monthly expenses were lower than Dave's monthly take-home pay. "Back to basics" was my theme as I started cutting out those things we would have to live without. Here's what we did:

- All telephone extras, such as call waiting and caller ID were cut.
- We cut premium cable channels. (We kept basic cable, since it would be our only source of entertainment at home.)
- Magazine subscriptions were terminated.
- The newspaper was cut down from a weekly subscription to Sunday only.
- Cellular phone and pager contracts were not renewed once they expired. (If Dave's employer paid for them, they were a keeper, but if we had to pay, we got rid of them.)

- Eating out was our huge budget cut, but it really brought us closer to our goal.
- Spending money and allowances were cut.
- We switched from a brand name diaper to a generic and it helped cut my diaper and wipes expenses in half. I found the generics to work just as well at almost half the cost.
- Not wanting to compromise on the brand and type of formula we used, a search through local stores allowed me to find the lowest cost per can. This expense would be lower as Colin got older (about 8 months) and drank less formula and began eating solid food.
- Birthday and Christmas gifts for friends were cut, and family gifts were slimmed down considerably.
- The clothing and activities budget got the axe.
- Dog toys and chewy treats were cut, but reward treats became smaller and less expensive. Dog food was bought two bags at a time when it was on sale.
- Since Colin was only in each clothing size range for about two months, I bought his clothes at a used clothing store. These stores are awesome! I bought well known, brand name clothing and toys at a fraction of the original cost and in good condition.

Once our new budget was complete, I sat down with Dave to review the plan. Wanting to make sure he was aware of the sacrifices we would have to make, I presented our options. After going over the stay-at-home budget and discussing our respective responsibilities and expectations with my staying home, we both knew where we stood.

Realizing our lifestyle would have to change, we both felt the trade-off would far exceed what we were giving up. I came to realize that staying home and raising our son in this day and age was a luxury instead of the norm. For a number of reasons, many moms have to go back to work and don't have this option. I felt incredibly grateful having this choice. So I traded in my briefcase for a diaper bag and took the leap of faith, to be a stay-at-home mom and write my book. It felt good; it felt right.

What I learned about being a stay-at-home mom:

- Get into a routine. The first two weeks will feel like vacation, but then boredom may set in. Having a routine will add a level of comfort and purpose. Plus, it will help your baby adjust to his new time with Mom.

- Start networking with other stay-at-home moms and be proactive. Plan weekly gatherings at the park, library, or mall. You will find other moms an incredible resource for information and a good source of adult conversation.

- Get out of the house! Try to leave the house every day, even if it's to go for a walk around the neighborhood, a drive to the post office, or visit a family member.

- Call your local library for a list of activities, such as story time and play hour. This is a great way to meet other moms with free entertainment. Free is good! While you are there, pick up a book for yourself.

- The food court at the local mall is an inexpensive, kid-friendly environment to meet friends for lunch. Pack your lunch if it doesn't fit into your budget.

- Don't substitute shopping as your purpose. When going to the mall or department stores to "browse," lock all methods of payment in your glove compartment. Eventually, you'll get used to looking and not buying. No sense tempting yourself with the credit card in your purse.

- E-mail is a great way to keep up with friends and keep contact with the outside world.

- Look at your budget as a game. Try to find ways to come "under budget" and store those savings in your savings account for a rainy day or date night out.

- Trade free babysitting time with another mom you trust. Each of you can pick a date night once a month. It guarantees one night a month with your spouse, without the burden of watching the clock or paying a babysitter. (The current rate for a babysitter is $5-$7 dollars an hour.)

- Make free time for yourself! Get out on your own! Have your husband watch the baby, so you can get out by yourself or with friends.

- After awhile, being on a budget and giving up the extras will be no big deal. You may find your "new life" is far richer than before you had your baby.

- Know that you will never regret making the decision to stay home with your child! It will be the time of your life!

Chapter 43

Getting In My Groove

At one point during this whole baby experience, I wondered when I would start feeling relaxed, comfortable, and confident with being a mom. Feeling as if I were floundering from one experience to another, I wondered if it would ever get better. When would I feel more in control, organized, and calm? When would I reach that point where I knew what I was doing? When would I get in a groove, where taking care of Colin and being a wife would be second nature? I guess my big question was:

When would I find that balance?

It wasn't any one event or situation that signified this momentous occasion. One day, I simply noticed that taking care of Colin, managing our household, and dealing with everyday life seemed to get much easier. With each first time experience, my confidence grew and I found myself more relaxed and going with the flow. My mind wasn't consumed with so many questions and feelings of hopelessness and panic. I came to the realization that we finally were in our groove, where our lives had become more comfortable, predictable, and adaptable. That's when I came to realize that life with a child is sort of like walking on a balance beam. After lots of practice, you get pretty good at it. When life throws you curves, like a sick child, or adapting to a new schedule, you may get knocked off balance, but you recover and keep going on.

It also hit me that I was experiencing one of the most significant times of my life. Bearing a child is the initiation into a very elite group with millions of members. No longer would I carry myself as a child. My role has transitioned from that of a child to that of a mother. I now had my own family, and it was my turn to be a mom and carry on the legacy.

Experiencing the many joys of parenthood for the first time was exciting and rewarding. It is something that will run through my mind for the rest of my life; remembering every detail, reliving each event. You see, we were creating memories, the very thing that makes our lives so rich and rewarding. The very thing that makes life worth living.

Only for a short period of time will I be a first time mom. Only once will I ever experience the newness and all the "first times" with my first child. We'll never forget witnessing such milestones as our baby smiling, rolling over, laughing, babbling, getting teeth, giving hugs, crawling, and walking. Only for a short period of time will I be a novice in the world of children. It is the first child that makes this event so magical, compelling us to go through it all again.

When I think back to the labor pains, the midnight feedings, the exhaustion, and the worry, it doesn't seem that bad anymore. The pain has dulled, the exhaustion is survivable, the work is burdening, but there is nothing that compares to the joy, pride, and rewards that come with having a child.

So, enjoy being a first time mom. Revel in it, enjoy the new experiences, the "first times," and take in the memories, because they will be the very things you live for. Through it all, I learned:

The most precious gift is life itself.

My Book of Lists

To Do Before Baby Arrives

Week 20

_____ Start thinking about designing your nursery.

Week 23

_____ Start looking for baby furniture (crib, changing table, dresser, bassinet, etc.).
- Specialized baby furniture can take 12 to 15 weeks to arrive. More common styles take 6-8 weeks. Some baby stores may have it in stock, but many don't keep high-priced items on the premises.

Week 27

_____ Register for baby items. See page 194 for a suggested list of items you may need.

Week 29

_____ Call your insurance company to:
- request the necessary maternity forms;
- find out at what hospital you are approved to have your baby;
- confirm the approved length of time for your hospital stay.

_____ Check with the human resources department at work regarding maternity leave paperwork.

Week 32

_____ Schedule:
- a tour of the hospital;
- Lamaze class;
- breastfeeding class;
- child care class;
- CPR training.

_____ Call the hospital and request the admittance forms be mailed to you.

_____ Start looking into day-care arrangements if you are going back to work. See page 190 for a list of suggested questions to ask providers.

Week 33

_____ Have your baby shower around this time. It will give you enough time to write thank you cards, go through the gifts to see what you have received, return duplicates, and make a list of remaining things you need.

_____ Wash all baby clothes.

Week 34

_____ Pick out boy and girl birth announcements before the baby arrives.

- Many stores will fill out the forms and hold them until you call with the birth information.
- Order the envelopes separately, so you can write the addresses on them while still pregnant. (I had to pay an extra $10 for shipping, but it was well worth addressing them beforehand. After the baby arrived, all I had to do was stuff the envelopes, enclose a picture, seal them, stick on a stamp, and have Dave mail them.)
- Don't forget to purchase enough stamps for the birth announcements.

_____ If breastfeeding, you may want to consider purchasing:

- Lansinoh breast cream; (I'm not one for brand recommendation, but it is the best to help with chapped nipples from nursing.)
- breast pump – electric or manual; (I used both. Most hospitals provide a free manual one, but you

have to remember to ask for it. Several hospitals also provide a free diaper bag and baby bottle cooler to keep bottles chilled.)

- two nursing bras and 3-5 pairs of nursing pads; (I liked the washable ones.)
- nursing gown; (They are so convenient in the middle of the night.)
- zip-locking sandwich bags and one-gallon zip-locking freezer bags for breast milk. (You also can use the baby bottle bags, but sandwich bags are less expensive.)

You may want to purchase:

- two boxes of sanitary pads with wings; (If you have any left over, you can use them when you get your period for the first time.)
- a box of prunes;
- over-the-counter pain medicine; (Extra Strength Tylenol, Ibuprofen, Advil, etc). Check with your doctor to see what he or she prefers.
- two firm, but inexpensive pillows with bright pillowcases; (So they don't get mixed in with the standard crappy, flat white hospital pillows.)
- one can of formula; (check with your doctor about which kind to use.)
- a keepsake box or some type of storage box for baby items;
- a first-year baby book and a small photo album; (Keep the small photo album in your diaper bag to show family and friends.)
- Infant medicine to have on hand for gas, pain, and fever relief because when you need it, the last thing you want to do is send your husband out at 3 a.m. while the baby is screaming his head off.

(I purchased **Infant** Mylicon, **Infant** Tylenol, **Infant** Advil.) *Check with your doctor first to get recommendations before purchasing and using.*

Week 35

_____ Type up your telephone call list. Make sure to include a check box to mark once the call was made. Be sure to include home and work telephone numbers.

_____ Arrange pet care and provide a house key and any instructions.

_____ Buy the remaining stuff you need for your baby.

_____ Finish the nursery.

_____ Put together the crib in the nursery.

- Put on the dust ruffle.
- Put the vinyl protector cover over the mattress (removing all trapped air), then put on the quilted mattress pad and then the crib sheet. Make sure the fitted sheet is pulled down tight, so it won't come loose. Put the mattress in the crib.
- Securely tie on the bumper pads.
- Put a waterproof pad in the center of the mattress. I threw a flat sheet over the crib to keep the dust out.

Week 36

_____ Purchase two boxes of thank you cards for gifts and flowers you will receive.

_____ Buy one book of stamps for thank you cards.

_____ Set up your changing table or Pack 'n Play with changing table feature downstairs.

- Open a pack of newborn diapers and stack them for easy access.
- Remove plastic wrap from wipes.

- Take diaper rash cream out of the box.
- Stack piles of sleepers, layettes, T-shirts.
- Store a pack of No. 1 diapers close by.
- Place an inexpensive waste basket next to the table for dirty clothes.
- Get your diaper pail ready.

_____ Put out the bottle warmer and set up a baby bottle drying rack next to the sink.

- Take bottles out of wrappers and wash them.

_____ Discuss with your doctor:

- when to call if you are having contractions;
- what emergency number to call;
- how the "doctor on call" situation is handled; (If not on call, when will the doctor be notified or will the doctor on call deliver your baby?)
- Birthing plans. (ie. natural or with the use of drugs)

Week 37

_____ Pack Lamaze bag and overnight bag. (See Packing Your Bags on Page 205 for a suggested list of items.)

_____ Install car seat and have it checked at local fire or police station.

_____ Address your birth announcement envelopes and put stamps on them.

_____ Set up the baby monitor.

Week 38

_____ Put together the baby swing and bouncy seat.

_____ Start cooking a week's worth of food and store it in the freezer.

_____ Stock up on family items, such as laundry detergent, paper towels, toilet paper, deodorant, soap, toothbrushes, toothpaste, contact solution, dishwashing detergent, liquid soap, pet food, and cereal. Running out of these items after you get home is a huge inconvenience.

Week 39

_____ Get organized! It may be six months before you find the time to read those magazines or put up those curtains.

_____ Give your house a good cleaning, so all you have to do is spot clean after the baby arrives.

_____ Ask three family members to buy the local newspaper on the day your baby is born for your keepsake box.

Week 40

_____ Spot clean your house.

_____ Send your spouse to the grocery store to purchase two weeks' worth of food. Make sure he buys roughage-type foods. (You may want to make a list or he'll come home with chips and beer.)

The Day You Go Into Labor

_____ Call pet sitters.

_____ Call employer and change voice mail and e-mail.

_____ Call your assistant birth coach if you have one.

Sample Day Care Questions

Over the Phone

1.   What are the hours of operation?_____
2.   Do they accept infants? _____
3.   How many children do they care for?_____
4.   What are their ages?_____
5.   What is the cost (per week)? _____
6.   Would you have an opening around (date)? _____

Personal Interview Questions for Site Visit

Remember to think long term.

Necessities:

1.   What am I expected to provide? (i.e. diapers, formula or breast milk in bottles, clothes, Pack 'n Play, etc.)
2.   If I'm breastfeeding, do you accept frozen milk or does it have to be in liquid form?
3.   How are the bottles heated, by microwave or bottle warmer?
4.   Does my child get his own personal storage space for his things?
5.   Do you permit the use of pacifiers, thumb sucking, or security blankets?

Care:

6.   What is the ratio of caregivers to newborns? Toddlers?
7.   What would a typical day be like at your facility?
8.   What types of snacks are given to the kids?
9.   Who determines the meal plans for the children?
10. What is the mealtime routine?

11. Do the children watch TV? If yes, how much and what do they watch?

12. What discipline is used?

13. How do you soothe a child who is crying or upset?

14. What is the routine for naptime? What if a child does not want to take a nap?

15. What do the children sleep on?

16. What is your approach to toilet training?

17. How do you make sure that each child receives individual attention?

18. Do the children go outside to play? How often?

19. Will the children leave the facility for off-site activities?

20. How will you communicate with me about, my child's progress?

21. Do you provide an activity report on what my child does each day?

22. How do you keep parents informed? Is there a message board?

23. What is your policy for parents being late to pick up their child?

Sick Child:

1. What is your policy for handling sick children?

2. What if you are unable to reach a parent?

3. Do you ever administer medicine?

4. How do you handle medical emergencies that may occur with the children?

5. What if you are ill?

Security:

1. What type of security measures do you have?

2. What is your policy for an adult, other than a parent, to pick up a child?

Provider Qualifications:

1. What kind of experience do you have caring for children?
2. Are you CPR certified?
3. Why did you choose this career?
4. How long have you been in this profession?
5. (Day care center question) What are your standards when choosing caregivers for your facility?
6. What do the children call you or the caregivers? Nanny? Ms. Debbie?
7. Who else will my child have contact with when they are in your care?

Payment:

1. Are the payments made weekly on a certain day?
2. Is there a procedure for this? (Nanny had us slip a check in a designated box so the children didn't see us paying for her care.)
3. Do we pay for weeks when we are on vacation?
4. Will you require a deposit to hold my baby's open position?
5. What days are you closed for business throughout the year?

Things to observe during a site visit:

- Is the location of the home or care center convenient and workable?
- Is the setting clean and organized?
- Is there a nice selection of toys that are in good shape?
- Is the equipment in safe working order? (i.e., Is the bouncy seat in good shape?)
- Is the caregiver interested in hearing about my child?

- How well do the children get along and are they taught to share and play nice?
- Does the caregiver seem to be enjoying herself in her work?
- Does she talk warmly and interact well with the children?
- Is the diaper changing area clean and organized?
- Do you see safety measures being taken? (Are outlets covered?)
- Do you have a good gut feeling about this place?

List of Suggested Baby Items to Register For

As you enter the baby store, you will be amazed at all the baby items. I bet there are more than 15,000 items available for every conceivable part of your baby's life. Some of them you will use, most of them you won't. Trying to create a standard or general list is very difficult, because everyone's life is different in some way. Coming up with the perfect list is impossible, but below is a checklist of all the things I found useful, along with the recommended quantity in parentheses. My list was created after talking to countless friends, my sisters, and my mom, who all have been involved with babies in some way. In addition, I read several books and took notes on what items were useful. Finally, I reviewed the list and arranged them in categories of usefulness, based on my experience. The following list is categorized under the following titles:

Used A Lot: Items I loved and used.
Personal Choice: Items I bought for my own reasons.
Toddler Items: Things you may use down the road.

Just write the name of the store on this page and happy registering!

Suggested Baby Items to Register For

Used A Lot

_____ Crib (1)

_____ Crib mattress (1)

_____ Vinyl crib mattress cover (1)

_____ Quilted crib mattress pad with elastic skirt (2)

_____ Crib sheets (2)

_____ Bumper pad (1)

A "bed in a bag" set usually comes with a comforter, one sheet, one dust ruffle, and bumper pad.

_____ Blankets (flannel for winter, cotton for summer) (4)

Deb told me not to use the comforter because most of them are too thick and may suffocate the baby. I put mine on the floor for Colin to play on.

_____ Changing table

I have one in my nursery and one in my dining room on the first floor. I use the one downstairs 10 times more than the one upstairs. Several of my friends use their Pack 'N Play downstairs with the changing table accessory.

_____ Changing table mattress (some may already come with them)

_____ Terry cloth changing table cover (2)

_____ Waterproof changing table pads (6)

These go over the terry cloth changing table cover cotton side up. This proved to be a LIFESAVER, because when it got dirty, I threw it in the hamper and put a fresh one on the table instead of having to continually wash the terry cloth cover.

_____ Dresser (1)

This can be the combination changing table and dresser unit.

_____ Baby monitor (1)

Make sure it has direct link privacy feature to scramble outside sounds. My sister's monitor could pick up the baby crying across the street. You also don't want your neighbors to hear your conversations through the monitor.

_____ Baby bathtub (1)

_____ Bathtub body sponge to hold baby in place (1)

_____ Baby shampoo, body wash, and lotion (1 of each)

_____ Hooded bath towels (2) and wash clothes (4)

_____ Baby hygiene care kit (1) (nail clippers, brush, etc.)

_____ Nasal aspirator –(1) unofficial name "booger sucker"

_____ Humidifier (1)

_____ Medicine (1 small bottle of each)

Infant Tylenol, Advil and Mylicon (approve this with your doctor first)

_____ Electric ear thermometer for taking the baby's temperature (1)

_____ Medicine dropper – (1) measurements in teaspoons and milligrams

_____ Stroller (1)

Cup holders; easy to open and collapse and lightweight; storage area for diaper bag; one hand pushing handle; wheels allow for quick turns; dark material to hide stains (several manufacturers have stroller, car seat and base all in one package).

_____ Car seat with base (1 or 2)

Lightweight; one button release for putting the handle up and down; harness points; easy grip Z shaped handle; canopy to block out sun; arm grips and hip-comfort fit. Base-level monitor to make sure it is level in the car. May want to get two bases if both parents will drop off or pick up from day care.

_____ U-shaped head support for car seat (1) – (if car seat doesn't come with one)

_____ Diaper bag (1)

One with several compartments; changing pad; medicine bag; tabs on zipper for easy opening; dark material to hide stains (My friends all raved about the Land's End and Eddie Bauer bags. I love my Land's End bag and it was reasonably priced.)

_____ Wipes container (1)

A flat, plastic container to hold wipes and keep them moist while in the diaper bag.

_____ Rocking chair or glider (1) –

I used this mostly for nighttime feedings in the nursery.

_____ Drain and dry bottle rack (1)

This goes next to your sink; make sure you get the one for baby bottles and not the one for sippy cups.

_____ Electric bottle warmer (1)

I used this a million times, whether I was breastfeeding or formula feeding. If I tapped into my supply of frozen breast milk, I thawed the bag of milk in a bowl of hot water. Next, I poured the milk in a baby bottle and then warmed it up in the bottle warmer. I also used it with formula. (Don't stick frozen breast milk bags in the bottle warmer because the bag may melt.)

_____ Breast pump if breastfeeding (1 or both)

Manual &/or electric: Most hospitals will provide a free manual pump if you ask them. Consider renting an electric pump if you plan to pump when you go back to work.

_____ Formula (1 can)

Remember, there is the possibility of your baby not settling well with milk-based or soy-type formulas.

Once you find the formula that works, stock up. Even if you are going to breastfeed, check with your doctor to see what type of formula you should get as a back-up. Even though I was breastfeeding, I bought a can of formula as my "absolute emergency" stash just in case we needed it. I didn't want to find myself at 3 in the morning with no milk, the baby crying and Dave driving down the street to the 24-hour grocery store. Remember, once you open the can, you have to use it by a certain time. Make sure you check the label.

_____ Baby bottles – (four 4oz. bottles and nine 8oz. bottles) This is a difficult call. There are 4-ounce bottles and 8-ounce ones. You will probably start out feeding your baby around 3 ounces of breast milk or formula eight times a day (every 3 hours). The smaller bottles are easy to hold and maneuver. But you eventually will grow into the big bottles. If you don't want the hassle, get the big bottles, and you'll eventually grow into them. I bought four little bottles and nine big bottles.

_____ Cloth diapers - (6) burp cloths

_____ Diapers and wipes
We ended up buying three packs of newborn diapers and a package of No. 1 diapers.

_____ Diaper rash cream (2)
One for your changing table, one for your diaper bag.

_____ Diaper pail (2)
One for upstairs, one for downstairs.

_____ Pack 'N Play (1)
Three-in-one feature containing bed, mid-high cradle and removable changing area.

_____ Bouncy seat (1)

_____ Battery powered swing with music (1)

List of Suggested Baby Items to Register For

_____ Activity gym (1)

_____ Exercise saucer (1)

_____ Pacifiers (0-3 month ones) (6-8)

_____ No-scratch mittens (1)

_____ Velcro bibs (4) (My order of preference – 1. Velcro, 2. snap, 3. pull over head, 4. tie-ons.)

Clothing: (amount indicated are individual items not number of packages)

_____ Side-snap T-shirts (3)

_____ Onesies (0-3 months) (6)

_____ Layettes (4-6)

_____ Sleepers with snaps in front (6-8)

_____ Newborn socks (4 pair)

_____ Cap (1)

Personal Choice

_____ Curved Side N Back Sleeper – looks like cheese wedges to keep baby on back

_____ Space heater for bathroom to keep baby warm during bath time

_____ Dreft laundry detergent – non-fragrant and hypoallergenic

_____ Soft-sided cooler for milk (many hospitals give to moms as a gift)

_____ Cooling packs (these are not provided by the hospital)

_____ Mattress for Pack 'N Play

_____ Pack 'N Play mattress sheet

_____ Mobile for baby's crib

_____ Classical music for babies on CDs

_____ Baby-view mirror for rear window (doesn't work well for SUVs or vans)

_____ Night-light for hallway

_____ Flannel crib sheet for winter

_____ Keepsake box

_____ Plastic utility toy bucket with rope handles

_____ Johnny jumping seat (started using around 4 months)
Clips to door frame, so baby can bounce up and down.
I liked the one with the tray and rubber padding
around it.

_____ Bathtub water thermometer

_____ Secure lock ratchet for car seat strap

_____ Baby videotapes

Toddler Items – Things to consider.

_____ Baby gates

_____ High chair with wheels

_____ Portable booster seat (can take to grandma's or friend's
house)

_____ Toddler car seat (for baby over 20 pounds)

_____ Umbrella stroller – When your baby is older (around 6
months), this is great for quick trips; you don't have to
haul the big stroller.

_____ Rubber-coated infant spoons

_____ No Spill Sippy cups

_____ Longer Velcro bibs

_____ Plastic cover for bathtub spout

_____ Bathtub ring or inflatable tub when baby outgrows
infant tub

_____ Bathtub toys

There were several lessons I learned about registering –
some of them the hard way and others came as advice from
my friends. Here is what I learned:

1. **It is never too early to register for your baby.**
There is no "rule" for when this can be done, but you

may want to wait until after the three-month waiting period. A good timeframe to begin this process is between weeks 20 to 24. This will allow you enough time to make your selections and allow for changes.

2. **Determine at what stores you would like to register.** Take into consideration the store's location to your home for returning items, their return policy, and how accessible the store is for family and friends. You may find that one store in your town is not available to family in another town or state. Another store may only allow returns with a receipt and within 30 days of the purchase. You may want to avoid stores with strict return policies. You will find yourself returning duplicate gifts, unused products, or incorrect items. The last thing you need to deal with is not having a receipt or having to return it by a specific date.

3. **If you have the time, go to one store with the biggest selection to familiarize yourself with all the baby items.** Don't register; just walk around and look at all the choices in each department. Doing this will allow you to become familiar with all the baby items and learn the layout of the store. It can be overwhelming the first time you enter a baby store and see the endless aisles and shelves of baby items. While you are browsing, look at baby furniture and determine what color of wood you like; what style of crib you prefer; whether you want a bed that converts into a toddler bed, and if you want a dresser and changing table. You don't need to make a decision that day, but at least you can leave the store with some ideas. Finally, take a walk through the bedding department. Look at all the various themes and accessories. This will help you determine the theme of your nursery. You don't have to

purchase your comforter set that day, but it will give you some ideas.

4. **Before you register, prepare a list of items, along with the quantity for each.** Break them down into categories, such as bedding, bathroom, nursery, clothing, big items. Having a list will allow you to cover all your bases and cut down on return trips. However, understand that you may find yourself returning to the store a few times to change your choices, add other items, or remove things you changed your mind on. (Hint: you may want to use the above list as your check-list.)

5. **Do not check your registry on the Internet.** Your registry on the Internet tells what items were purchased, so it may ruin the surprise of what you will get at your baby shower. I did this and was so disappointed with myself.

The Big Event

When it came time for me to register, I was so excited and, again, I was clueless. I was unprepared for this big event and therefore learned some lessons the hard way. Here are my recommendations for the day you register for your baby:

- The first recommendation is to leave your partner at home the first time you go, *unless* he is the type of person you think can tolerate two or three hours looking at baby stuff. Dave loves to shop, but I knew he quickly would get bored with all the strollers, high chairs, bouncy seats, monitors, etc. I could picture it: Me in my glory and excitement asking him, "Which bouncy seat should we get? How about this one? It has a vibrator and activity rack. I love the pattern and the quality of the material. What do you think?" His reply,

"I don't care, just pick one." "What? Just pick one? How could you say that!" I basically told him I would register for the items I thought we needed and then I'd bring him back and show him what we registered for. I told him we could change anything or return it if we found something better. Dave agreed to this arrangement. I think he was relieved not to go, or was that me?

- My second recommendation is to take a friend who has had a baby, if you are not bringing your spouse. She will be able to tell you what she used and what was a dud. In addition, she can teach you what half of the stuff is for. Remember one thing: Everyone is different. There may be things you really like and think you'll use, while other stuff your friend used, you think you'll never touch. I took Linda, who spent a good deal of time around our nephews and saw what Deb used. I wish I had asked Deb to come with us. With three boys, she would have known what everything in the store was for.

- The third recommendation is go to register during "off" hours. The weekend is probably not a good time to register, because that is when everyone else is getting caught up. With lots of people and kids pouring through the aisles, it is difficult to navigate around, experiment with various baby equipment, and most important, find a sales person to answer questions. Consider going on a weeknight or a Friday or Saturday night.

- Fourth, make sure you are physically ready to register. Go when you are well rested and wear comfortable shoes and clothes and make sure you've eaten or bring a snack. You may find yourself in the store for several hours and on your feet the entire time. With standing, bending, and squatting down, you may get warm. All this physical activity and brainpower may give you the "hungries." If there is one thing I've learned about being pregnant, it's to keep food handy.

- Fifth, make sure you have a list of items you have decided on and a pen. As you register for each item, cross it off your list. Write down next to any item why you did not register for it. This will help later when you review your list to see if you need to go to register this item at another store or come back and add it to the list.

- Make sure your registry is available on the Internet if the store provides this service. It is so convenient and will save time for family and friends.

- Finally, have fun with it! This is truly a wonderful experience and really helps you prepare for the birth of your baby.

Packing Your Bags

Overnight Hospital Bag

For You

_____ Loose-fitting clothes to come home in.

_____ Two pair of maternity underwear, just in case you don't want to wear the hospital ones.

_____ Nursing bra and pads

_____ Nursing gown and robe

- I would recommend using the hospital gowns during your stay. Your nursing gown may get dirty, so you might as well trash the hospital gowns instead of your own.

_____ Slippers

_____ Makeup, deodorant, lotion, toothbrush and toothpaste, hair spray

_____ Blow dryer

_____ Curling iron

_____ Breast pump if you want to talk to the lactation specialist about it.

- A consultation with the lactation specialist is free and available to everyone.

_____ Paper and pen (to record when to take medicine and to compile a thank you list)

For Your Baby

_____ Baby book (to get footprints)

_____ Baby outfit (don't forget socks if the outfit doesn't have feet)

- Remember: The car seat strap goes between the baby's legs, so you may want to avoid layette outfits.

_____ Cap

_____ Pacifier

_____ Baby blanket and snowsuit (if it's winter)

_____ Car Seat

Lamaze Bag

_____ Lip balm

_____ Breath spray

_____ Focal point item

_____ Watch with a second hand

_____ Magazines

_____ Warm cotton socks

_____ Telephone contact list

_____ Two firm pillows with bright-colored pillow cases, so you don't leave them in the birth room.

_____ Walkman with a few CDs, if you think you'll use it. (I found the TV more useful, because it also visually took my mind off of things.)

_____ Glasses or contact lenses with solution and storage case

_____ Ponytail holder or barrette

_____ Your doctor's contact information

_____ Pack of crackers in case you are hungry after the baby is born.

Labor partner's Lamaze bag

_____ Sweatshirt, sweatpants

_____ Magazines

_____ Roll of quarters for vending machines and pay phone

_____ Snacks

_____ Money for meals

_____ Camera with film, batteries

_____ Camcorder with extra power pack and tapes

_____ Toothbrush, toothpaste

_____ Sleepwear, toiletries, and clothes for the next day

Labor Coach Responsibilities

Things for the birthing coach to do:

1. Set out the focal point, breath spray, and lip balm. Find out where to get ice chips.

2. When you get to the hospital, familiarize yourself with the surroundings. Where are the ice chips, extra pads for the labor bed, blankets, thermostat, nurses station, waiting room, TV remote control, shower if your partner wants to take one to relax. (Some hospitals don't have a shower in the labor room; you have to go down the hall.)

3. Learn the name of your labor nurse and take a good look at what she looks like. Should you need to find her for something, it helps to know her name.

4. Be the eyes and ears for your partner. The nurse will not be in the room during the entire time she is in labor. At times, nurses may come in with medicine or need to check on her. The mom will find herself trying to get through the contractions, so her sense of focus and memory may not be strong. This is where you come in. It is your responsibility to ask questions and help mommy understand what is going on. Her focus will be on dealing with the contractions, so it's the labor coach's task to watch your partner. What kind of medication are they giving her? Does it fit the guidelines of what you discussed? Does she need ice chips, a blanket, to go to the bathroom? The last thing you want to do is argue with a woman in labor, but you need to be her eyes and ears for what you both agreed on, such as drugs.

5. Get ice chips.

6. Hold her hand.

7. Do the breathing with her. It will keep her focused and encourage her to keep up the breathing until the contraction subsides.

8. Coach when contractions are coming and going away. When you get into the birthing room and your partner is being hooked up to the monitors, ask the nurse to teach you how to read the contraction indicator. There is a small, numeric screen on the equipment that will display a number based on the level and consistency of the contraction. This is very useful when you want to get your partner ready for the next contraction. This will help her to focus and concentrate on her breathing. I found it so useful when Dave would tell me when one was coming, talk me through it, and let me know when the numbers started to go down. That was such a relief to know when the contraction was going away.

9. Don't do anything until the contraction is over. During a contraction, it is so difficult to deal with anything other than focusing on the breathing. I found I could only deal with one thing at a time. I was having a contraction when the anesthesiologist was talking to me. Dave stepped in and asked her to wait until the contraction was over. I just couldn't deal with anything until the contraction went away.

10. Wipe a cool washcloth on her forehead and neck, but ask her first.

11. Give positive encouragement; this is so important because it can get tiring and defeating after several hours of discomfort and pain.

12. Take pictures; this is something we didn't do and I regret it. We were so excited about the baby, we forgot to grab the camera.

13. If you don't have a video camera, borrow one. I'm so glad we took video. Make sure you get the video camera out and film a few words before going to the hospital. Once there, and between contractions, say the time, how many centimeters, what your status is and any other comments. Linda remembered to do this, and I was so glad. It was so special to look back on the video and relive it. Most hospitals will not let you tape the birth, for legal reasons, but they will let you take pictures and video after the baby arrives.

Leaving the Hospital

_____ Did you fill out all necessary paperwork?

_____ Did you ask for your free manual breast pump?

_____ Did you see the lactation specialist?

_____ Do you have your prescriptions?

_____ Is your car seat base and carrier installed in the car? (Don't bring the carrier into the hospital; mom and baby must leave in a wheelchair.)

_____ Did you grab a few ice pack pads?

To Do When You Get Home

_____ Call your employer to get the baby on insurance. You usually have 30 days, but confirm this.

_____ Call your baby's doctor to schedule a two-week appointment.

_____ Schedule your six-week appointment.

_____ Mail mortgage payment and bills. It's so easy to forget this.

_____ Order birth announcements, get copies of a picture to include, and mail them.

_____ Start writing and mailing thank you cards.

_____ Call your church about scheduling the religious ceremony.

_____ Call your day-care provider and send them a birth announcement.

_____ Order your baby's birth certificate.

_____ Call your lawyer to change your Living Will. If you don't have one, you may want to get one in place. Decide who will raise your child if something happens to you and your spouse. Make sure your Will is as detailed as possible. As morbid as it may seem to have to deal with this, it is the responsible thing to do.

Things to Remember When You Get Home

- Communicate, communicate, and communicate with your spouse. He can't read minds.
- Compliments not criticism; praise instead of pick. If your spouse loads the dishwasher wrong, who cares, as long as it gets done!
- Know when you are at your limit and step away.
- Ask for help and use it to your advantage!

What to Put in Your Diaper Bag

_____ One-gallon zip locking bags for dirty diapers and clothes

_____ Flat, plastic wipes container

_____ Four diapers

_____ One onesie, two sleepers, one pair of socks, one cap

_____ One blanket

_____ A pacifier

_____ Medicine pouch: baby gas and pain relief medicine, a tampon, pad and aspirin

Sample Schedules

One of the biggest sources of frustration for me came after Colin was on a schedule. As he got older, his awake time and naps started getting longer, so I never knew when to feed him. With Deb's coaching and suggestions, Colin's schedules for the first year went something like this.

3 weeks old to 2 months
(3-hour schedule)

6 a.m.	I got up and nursed Colin.
9 a.m.	I got up and nursed Colin.
Noon	I nursed Colin, pumped a bottle, and then put in the freezer.
3 p.m.	I nursed Colin, and pumped a bottle for the midnight feeding.
6 p.m.	I nursed Colin.
9 p.m.	I nursed Colin, passed him to Dave to burp, and I went to bed.
12 a.m.	Dave fed Colin one of the pumped bottles.
3 a.m.	After six hours of sleep, I got up and nursed the baby.

2 months old to 4 months
(Colin's eating while at day care)

7 a.m.	Woke Colin up, nursed him, and changed his diaper.
10 a.m.	Nanny fed him a bottle.
1 p.m.	Nanny fed him a bottle.
4 p.m.	Nanny fed him a small bottle, so he would nurse when we got home.

6 p.m.	I nursed him from my full boobs (I usually pumped at 2:30 p.m.).
9:00 p.m.	I nursed Colin, passed him to Dave to burp, and I pumped a bottle.
12:00 a.m.	Dave fed him a bottle, burped him, and put him to bed.
4:00 a.m.	I nursed Colin.

4 months to 7 months

(Colin's schedule once I stayed home. I fed him when he woke up and before he went to sleep.)

7:00 a.m.	Colin woke up, I changed his diaper and fed him a bottle with formula and rice cereal.
7:00 – 9:00 a.m.	I kept Colin awake.
9:00 a.m.	I fed him a bottle.
9:15 – 11:15 a.m.	Colin took a nap. When he woke up, I changed his diaper and fed him a bottle.
11:45 – 2:30	I kept Colin awake.
2:30 p.m.	I fed him a bottle and put him to bed.
2:30 – 4:30 p.m.	Colin took his afternoon nap. When he woke up, I changed his diaper and fed him a bottle.
4:30 – 7:00 p.m.	I kept Colin awake.
7:00 – 7:30 p.m.	I fed Colin a small bottle, then let him take a 30-minute "power nap."
7:30 – 9:15 p.m.	I kept Colin awake. He turned into a monster as we got closer to 9:15.)
9:15 p.m.	I changed his diaper, put on his pajamas and made his bedtime bottle.
9:40 p.m.	Dave fed 8 ounces to Colin and tried to get him to drink it all.

9:55 p.m.	Dave put Colin to bed.
	(After five months, Colin started sleeping through the night, which eliminated the 5 a.m. feeding.)
7 a.m.	Colin woke up.

7 months to 1 year

7:00 – 7:30 a.m.	Colin wakes up. I change his diaper and mix 4 ounces of formula with rice cereal, a small amount of fruit for taste and spoon feed him.
7:30 – 9:30 a.m.	I keep him awake and we played.
9:30 a.m.	I feed him a 4-ounce bottle and put him to bed.
9:40 – 11:15 a.m.	Colin takes a nap.
11:30 a.m.	He wakes up. I change his diaper and feed him lunch.
12:15 – 3 p.m.	Put him in the Johnny jumpy seat while I take a shower. Then run errands, go to play group, and keep Colin awake.
3:00 p.m.	I feed Colin a 6-ounce bottle and put him to bed for a nap.
4:30 p.m.	I wake Colin up, change his diaper and feed him dinner.
4:30 – 8:30 p.m.	I keep Colin awake.
8:30 p.m.	Changed his diaper, fed him an 8-ounce bottle and put him to bed for the evening.

Other Things I Learned

- I learned that two packages of newborn diapers and one package of number ones was plenty to start out with. I also learned that unopened packages of diapers could be returned to the store.
- I learned to watch my son's weight and compare it to the weight range on the diaper package. When we had consecutive "blowouts" – poop shooting up his back or wet clothes – it usually meant we were at the tail end of that diaper size.

  Approximate diaper ranges
  - Newborns - 6-10 pounds
  - No. 1: 8-14 pounds
  - No. 2: 12-18 pounds
  - No. 3: 16-28 pounds
  - No. 4: 22-37 pounds
  - No. 5: 27+ pounds
  - No. 6: 35+ pounds
- Several times, Colin woke up wet in the middle of the night, so I started putting the next size up on him at bedtime. If he wore a No. 2 during the day, I'd put a No. 3 on him at bedtime.
- It always seemed to catch us off guard when he was ready for the next size. I found it so convenient to buy a package of the next size diaper and store it in the closet. Colin quickly went through newborn, No. 1 and No. 2, but he stayed in No. 3 for a while.
- As Colin got older, I went from changing his diaper every three hours (eight times a day) to every four hours (six times a day), and I finally settled on five times a day. (Remember, once they start sleeping through the night, that takes 10 hours.)

- I learned that Colin spent the first three months in sleepers, because it was too much work to put him in infant pants and shirts. (Avoid outfits with snaps down the back. It's like dressing Jell-O.) I should have returned most of the outfits in the 0-3 month size range because he never wore half of the stuff. That way, I could have used a store credit to buy a really nice out-fit for his formal pictures. If you don't think you'll use some clothes, return them for store credits, then go back and buy a nice outfit when you need it.

- I learned that teaching Colin to eat from a spoon was more difficult than I thought. It took two weeks and a lot of messy faces before he learned to open his mouth and maneuver the food to the back of his throat to swallow.

- When traveling with our baby, I put several one-gallon ziplock bags in my diaper bag. They make excellent traveling diaper pails and are convenient for dirty clothes.

- Many of my mom friends said a diaper bag with many compartments works the best for keeping the dirty items away from the clean stuff. I agree.

- I learned that Dave and I would develop what we called "the poop report" as every day, we monitored Colin's diapers to make sure he wasn't getting constipated.

- I learned that I would grow to love stores with big grocery carts to hold Colin's carrier; automatic doors; changing tables in bathrooms; elevators for the stroller; breastfeeding stations; and wheelchair access bath-rooms, so the stroller and I could fit in the bathroom at the same time.

- Three weeks after I stopped breastfeeding, I got my period. Remember what that is?

- Line-dry your nursing tops and maternity clothes. The dryer will shrink your clothes and shrinkage is not a good thing.
- When going out to dinner, ask for the bill when your food arrives, so you can pay it quickly. This allows a quick getaway, should the baby start throwing a fit. Early on, eating out was so easy because the baby slept the entire time, but when he reached about 12 weeks, it started getting difficult. By 10 months, you'll be eating fast food or at family friendly restaurants.

BIBLIOGRAPHY

(1) *Your Pregnancy and Birth.* A guide for prepared childbirth from the health professionals at OhioHealth. Avery Publishing Group, Inc. 1997. p. 62, 63.

(2) *Your Pregnancy and Birth.* A guide for prepared childbirth from the health professionals at OhioHealth. Avery Publishing Group, Inc. 1997. p. 62, 63.

(3) Johnson, M.D., Robert V. *Mayo Clinic Complete Book of Pregnancy & Baby's First Year.* William Morrow and Company, Inc. 1994. p. 425, 426.

(4) Johnson, M.D., Robert V. *Mayo Clinic Complete Book of Pregnancy & Baby's First Year.* William Morrow and Company, Inc. 1994. p. 426.

ORDER FORM

To order additional copies of *first time Mom* directly from the publisher, send the order form along with your check or money order to:

CMB Production
P.O. Box 815
Hilliard, OH 43026

Send (___) copies of *first time Mom* by Wendy Beahn to:

_____

First Name   Last Name

_____

Address

_____

City   State   Zip

_____ Copies at $10.95 each =_____
Qty.   Cost of Book(s)

Tax, Shipping & Handling   + $4.95

Total

_____

Visit our website at
http://www.firsttimeMomOnline.com